Why are we

An Analysis of Hospi

JOHN YATES

*Inter-Authority Comparisons and Consultancy,
Health Services Management Centre,
Birmingham*

Oxford   New York   Tokyo

OXFORD UNIVERSITY PRESS

1987

Oxford University Press, Walton Street, Oxford OX2 6DP

Oxford   New York   Toronto
Delhi   Bombay   Calcutta   Madras   Karachi
Petaling Jaya   Singapore   Hong Kong   Tokyo
Nairobi   Dar es Salaam   Cape Town
Melbourne   Auckland
and associated companies in
Beirut   Berlin   Ibadan   Nicosia

Oxford is a trade mark of Oxford University Press

Published in the United States
by Oxford University Press, New York

British Library Cataloguing in Publication Data
Yates, John, 1943 Nov. 15-   .
Why are we waiting?: an analysis of
hospital waiting lists. — (Oxford medical
publications)
1. Hospitals — Great Britain — Admission
and discharge.
I. Title.
362.1' 1   RA971.8
ISBN 0-19-261674-9 (pbk.)

Library of Congress Cataloging in Publication Data
Yates, John.
Why are we waiting?
(Oxford medical publications)
Includes index.
1. Hospitals — Great Britain — Waiting lists.
2. Medicine — Practice — Great Britain.   3. National
Health Service (Great Britain)   I. Title.   II. Series.
RA986.Y38   1987   362.1' 1' 0941   87-11161
ISBN 0-19-261674-9 (pbk.)

Set by Dobbie Typesetting Service, Plymouth
Printed in Great Britain by
Richard Clay Ltd
Bungay, Suffolk

Preface

This preface is a personal note which allows me to express my frustration, my bias, and my thanks.

I wrote this book because I have become increasingly uncomfortable as I move in two circles. In my professional life I talk to doctors, managers, academics, and journalists, who discuss waiting-lists dispassionately. In my private life I meet neighbours, friends, and relatives, who discuss waiting-lists with growing hostility and emotion. You would not think they were talking about the same subject. When I started to lecture on this subject and began to gather together the rough manuscript for this book, a number of friends and colleagues commented on the clever device that I had used in presenting an imaginary patient called Mrs G (see Chapter 1). I was taken aback. This is not a novel, and Mrs G is a real person who has not sought any publicity for her own particular case.

One of the more contentious issues in examining waiting-lists is the subject of private practice. A high level of emotion is frequently engendered, particularly amongst those who hold very different political points of view. We all have our prejudices on this subject and I cannot pretend that my analysis is wholly objective. What I can do is state my bias openly. As a Christian I identify with people like David Sheppard on the views expressed in his book *Bias to the poor*. I am concerned less about changing the current system where state medicine and private medicine are allowed to exist side by side, than I am with clarifying the extent to which this system is abused and correcting that situation. Waiting-lists are an example of where the poorer members of society suffer and the richer members of society gain. The literature of the NHS for over 30 years has shown that ill-health is more common amongst the elderly and the poor. Like other parts of the NHS, waiting-lists have a high proportion of such citizens, most of whom are unable to pay for private medical care. It is for that reason that private medicine has a very limited contribution to make in the reduction of waiting-lists.

I would like to express my thanks to one or two people who have provided help and advice in my efforts to complete this book in the last few months. Eric Sweet has worked hard to bring life into the dull diagrams which I first laid on his desk. There are many who have spent time reading various drafts, in particular Pat Lakeman and three consultant surgeons whose blushes I will spare. I must also thank my family who have their weekends interrupted whilst 'Daddy does his book'. Finally there are my four close colleagues who have helped me put so much of the material together—Mike Davidge, Mike Harley, Lorna Vickerstaff, and Kate Wood. As on previous occasions, without Lorna's help and encouragement the manuscript would never have been completed. Having made these acknowledgments, the responsibility of producing a book which contains both fact and emotion must lie with myself.

Birmingham
May 1987   J. Y.

Contents

1   A cry from the heart, hernia, hip . . .   1

2   Don Quixote's windmills—waiting-lists are irrelevant   8

3   The axe and the iceberg—waiting-lists are inevitable   20

4   Money, money, money—waiting-lists are caused by under-funding   29

5   The corpulent bureaucrat—waiting-lists are caused by inefficiency   38

6   The hypocritical oath—waiting-lists are caused by selfishness   48

7   What is it like so far?—summarizing the evidence   63

8   What has been tried?   68

9   What should be tried?   80

Index   91

CONTENTS

1

A cry from the heart, hernia, hip . . .

How is it that a National Health Service, sometimes regarded as the envy of the world, can leave my neighbour in pain and suffering? It was over five years ago that Mrs G first saw an orthopaedic surgeon. He diagnosed a back condition which required an operation and put her on the waiting-list. There she stays and her condition slowly deteriorates. During these five years my children have grown up watching the lady next door becoming more and more stooped as she moves around her kitchen or walks in her garden. She is in constant pain, but puts a brave face on it. The hospital Mrs G attends has over 2000 patients on the orthopaedic waiting-list alone and many of the patients have had to wait for years. In my efforts to comfort her, I find myself making reassuring noises and defend the NHS by saying, 'I'm sure they are doing their best'. Like fishermen exchanging tales about the size of their catch, we start to tell stories about other peoples' waiting experience. 'How is Gordon doing?' she says. Gordon lives two doors away from us and he too is on a waiting-list. He is a fellow in his early fifties, a very active man who was an excellent sportsman. In his time he played a very high standard of club cricket, but now I watch him with his arthritic hip and his walking stick as he passes the end of our drive, looking like a man of eighty. The circle widens. We talk about an eighty-year-old aunt who is having to wait ten months for an out-patient appointment and I tell Mrs G of a 25-year-old relative who has been told that she has to wait three months for an out-patient appointment to see a gynaecologist, following the discovery of abnormal cells in a cervical smear test. Mrs G expresses sympathy for the younger woman. For a moment she seems almost humbled as I bring the conversation to an end by explaining to her that she is just one of over half a million people in a similar plight in this country.

As if these ridiculous statements make the pain any easier! I might as well make her feel guilty for being ill and tell her how lucky she is not to be starving in Ethiopia.

Over half a million people are waiting for admission to a hospital bed and the majority are waiting for surgical operations in five specialties — general surgery, orthopaedics, gynaecology, ophthalmology, and ear, nose, and throat surgery. They are waiting for operations which surgeons regard as relatively straightforward, for conditions such as hernias, varicose veins, hip replacements, hysterectomies, cataracts, and tonsils and adenoids. There are lesser numbers waiting to be operated on by other specialists like urologists, plastic surgeons, and oral surgeons. As technology advances there is also a growing waiting-list for transplants of various types. Whilst the numbers waiting for transplant surgery are relatively small, as compared with the bulk of the waiting-list, the patients on these lists receive much attention because their medical conditions are invariably life-threatening. Heart, kidney, and lung transplantation is not simply interesting for the media, but also critical for the patient. The vast majority of people on waiting-lists, however, are not under threat of death, but nevertheless they wait in varying degrees of pain and discomfort, often having a restricted life-style and sometimes being unable to work.

Since the Health Service was established in 1948 there has been no real reduction in the number of people waiting for treatment. Figure 1 shows that in the first 25 years of the NHS's existence the list remained close to half a million, then between 1973 and 1982, rose sharply to over three quarters of a million. Whilst this mountain of people waits, the rest of us argue about the reasons for the list's existence and whether it underestimates or over-estimates the true demand for health care. But that is only half the story — whilst one in every hundred of us is on a waiting-list, many would argue that Mrs G is lucky because she has at least got on to the waiting-list. To reach that stage she had first to see her general practitioner and then be referred by him to a consultant orthopaedic surgeon. For Mrs G that meant an additional wait of several months — but that was over five years ago. Today

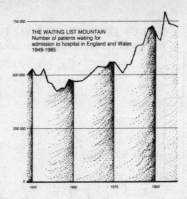

Fig. 1.

Mrs G's neighbours have to wait over a year simply to see an orthopaedic consultant and only then do they begin to 'serve their time' on the waiting-list for admission. The NHS counts the thousands who wait for an operation, but fails to count the thousands simply waiting to see a consultant.

Not the NHS?

Mrs G, like many others, believes that she is waiting for treatment in a national health service. She is not. She is waiting for treatment in one of over 250 local health services in Britain. In 1985 the size of the orthopaedic waiting-lists in the English and Welsh districts alone varied from those with less than 100 patients to one which had 4089 patients. Figure 2 shows how the size of waiting-lists varies from district to district. Dare I tell Mrs G that she is waiting for treatment in one of the seven districts having over 2000 patients? Whether you count the size of waiting-lists for admission, measure the amount of time spent getting on to the waiting-list, or the time actually spent on the waiting-list, the variation is enormous. If Mrs G were to be referred to an orthopaedic surgeon today, she could wait for one week or one year for an out-patient appointment—just depending on where

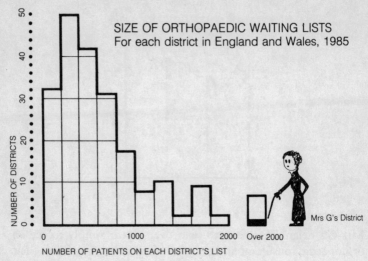

Fig. 2.

she lives! In Great Britain health care is in the hands of district health authorities. The territory covered can range from districts like Islington or Bloomsbury which have a few square miles of densely populated London, to districts which cover larger and much more sparsely populated areas like Northumberland, Powys, and the Highlands. The average district has a population of about a quarter of a million, but there are huge variations such as that which leaves Leicestershire's district of 860 000 people bordering on to Rugby's 87 000. None of this would matter if they each had an appropriate share of hospitals and staff, but unfortunately this is not the case. The distribution of resources is imperfect and some parts of the country are very badly provided for, whilst others are relatively well-blessed. Not only are there variations in the level of resources, but there are also huge variations in the performance of those districts. Whether you choose to measure the size of waiting-lists, the length of waiting time, the throughput of patients, the success rate of operations, or even the hospital death rate, you will find the most unnerving variations from one part of the country to another. The NHS embraces the under-funded and the over-funded, the efficient and the wasteful, the hard-working and the lazy, the highly professional and the dishonest, and the breathtakingly skilful and the dangerous. Variety is the spice of NHS life!

Despite the fact that almost three quarters of a million people are waiting for admission, not everyone has to wait like Mrs G. I could write a much more optimistic book about the NHS telling the story of how family, neighbours, and friends have been treated speedily and successfully by skilful and hard-working staff. There are parts of the service where patients are treated without unnecessarily lengthy waits. Given that this is the case, why must pain and suffering be distributed in some unexplained and apparently random fashion? What could the better parts of the NHS teach Mrs G's district? Is it not possible for waiting-lists and waiting times to be reduced significantly?

Dreary old answers?

It is of no comfort to Mrs G to know that she is one of half a million who are waiting. The next time I go into my garden to cut the hedge, what excuse will I offer to my neighbour for her long wait? As a 'professional' in the NHS I have heard many explanations from clinicians, managers, politicians, economists, and others, but there are five which are repeatedly rehearsed by their many advocates.

1. *The statistics are too inaccurate to use*
There are so many errors in the data collected and so much data that we do not collect, that many believe waiting-lists are simply irrelevant. They are like Don Quixote's windmills—figments of the imagination. Thus we are discouraged from studying waiting-lists because they make no contribution to measuring the need or demand for health care.

2. *Waiting-lists will always exist*
This argument is one of resigned inevitability. There is always more to be done than resources will allow and thus some form

of rationing has to be adopted. Waiting-lists provide that rationing mechanism and thus simply act as the boundary between what we can do and what we would like to do. This is a strong and depressing argument.

3. More resources are required

The NHS appears to be significantly under-funded compared with health services in other comparable countries in the Western world. If the NHS is provided with more resources it will treat more patients and reduce the waiting-lists.

4. The NHS is inefficient

Many who come into contact with the NHS can give illustrations of wasted resources. One typical example occurred when the Chairman of the Conservative Party visited a friend who was being treated in a 42-bedded NHS eye hospital. When Mr Tebbit went round the hospital one Thursday afternoon there were four patients present, despite the fact that the same hospital had 1500 patients on its waiting-list. Efficiency experts from commerce and industry believe that this sort of story can be repeated elsewhere and far too frequently and they feel that a dose of good management would soon reduce the waiting-lists.

5. One service for the rich and another for the poor

There are occasions when the selfishness of health service staff at all levels is seen to contribute to increased pain and suffering for the very patients they claim to serve. Industrial action and private medicine may seem strange bedfellows, but both are seen to contribute to larger waiting-lists.

As the winter draws in I have a few months before I next cut my hedge—a few more months to decide which explanation to use when I next meet Mrs G over the privet. I have time to look more closely at the evidence which supports or contradicts these arguments. The next five chapters of this book look at each of the five 'excuses' and examine the evidence. Three types of evidence are presented, drawing on individual cases, detailed studies of some of the largest waiting-lists in the country, and on the statistical information that is available. These individual cases I use are from personal experience and are not tales which have grown in the telling. The detailed studies come from a survey[1] that is at present being undertaken of 33 waiting-lists in 10 districts. These 33 lists represent almost 10 per cent of the country's waiting-lists and over 15 per cent of the patients who have had to wait over a year for treatment. It is probably the largest survey of waiting-list patients ever undertaken. The statistical information used is that which is routinely collected in the NHS for every hospital in England and Wales. By using these three sources I should be able to produce some evidence which explains why my neighbour has to wait so long for treatment, because Mrs G and her half million friends are getting tired of hearing the same old excuses.

In recent years the waiting-list debate has been about whether the number will increase or decrease. We seem to have accepted that it should be there and no longer challenge its presence. It is just part of the British way of life, like Big Ben, bobbies on bicycles, and cups of tea. If we simply claim that waiting-lists are a British disease, the patient's response will eventually become more radical and demands will increase for an improved system. I submit that the problem is now urgent enough to warrant immediate attention. It is time to challenge a part of the British way of life.

Reference

1. Davidge, M., Harley, M., Vickerstaff, L., and Yates, J. (1987). The anatomy of large inpatient waiting lists. *Lancet*, 1, 794–6.

2

Don Quixote's windmills?

Waiting-lists are irrelevant

The argument

Don Quixote was a crazy Spanish knight who spent much of his lifetime trying to rid the countryside of giants. The giants turned out to be in his imagination and in reality he was only tilting at windmills. Those of us who make a serious attempt to concern ourselves with the waiting-lists are frequently accused of being like Don Quixote—wasting our time on an illusory problem. We are told by statisticians, epidemiologists, managers, and doctors that waiting-list information is so inaccurate that no reliance can be placed on the figures. They tell us that waiting-lists:

- include patients who will never be operated on;

- fail to include patients who require treatment;

- only give half the story because out-patient waiting time is excluded; and,

- do not give any idea of waiting time.

It is argued that time spent studying waiting-lists will be a wasted paper exercise, which will make no contribution to the improvement of health care. Quite simply, waiting-lists are seen as irrelevant.

The evidence

Inflated lists?

Figure 1 shows the annual count of all patients on the waiting-list on 31 December for each year since 1949. This simple little graph causes considerable mirth amongst medical staff, nurses, and anyone with a knowledge of how the NHS collects data. If any organization can make a mess of collecting data it is the NHS. You might think that counting how many people are on a waiting-list would be an easy task, but it often proves to be difficult to track down the many card indexes, record books, and other documents which record the facts. I was recently involved in the study of a gynaecology waiting-list in a London teaching district. For a number of years the waiting-list figures had shown that there were between 1000 and 1400 patients on the list and that the list was steadily growing. When we examined the actual waiting-list cards to see what sort of conditions patients were waiting for, the clerks could only find 700 cards. Nobody could explain how the waiting-list was only half that which was recorded! If every other hospital in the country recorded its data in a similar fashion we could soon see a massive reduction in waiting-lists! We must, however, learn to be wary of using this sort of evidence when discussing waiting-lists. Many people within the NHS and some politicians are given to arguing from the specific to the general. Stories of this sort make for interesting illustrations, but we must be cautious, and not produce sensational generalizations. In the past nine months my examination of a further 33 huge waiting-lists has revealed no case in which the number of waiting-list cards substantially differed from the number recorded on the list.

A more serious problem is the reliability of the information about those patients who are on the waiting-list. From time to time consultants and health authorities review their waiting-lists and find that some of the patients on the list no longer need or want an operation, or occasionally have already had their operation. It is slightly disconcerting to find that some waiting-lists include patients who do not require an operation. It may be that the symptoms have improved, the patient has learned to live with the discomfort, or that the patient has died from the illness concerned or a different illness. Occasionally a doctor places a patient on the list anticipating a longer wait than actually occurs and on admission the patient is not yet ready for an operation. Some of these reasons show how difficult it is for a clinician to assess accurately the need for an operation and one sometimes wonders whether occasionally waiting-lists are used as a form of treatment!

The evidence published in some journals to support the fact that waiting-lists are inflated is quite impressive.[1,2,3] A typical example came from the orthopaedic service in Leicester. The orthopaedic division wrote to 950 patients on the waiting-list, all of whom had been on the list for over a year. Before even sending out the letters they discovered that 193 of the patients had already had the operation in the hospital, but that their names had not been removed from the list. Having written to the remainder of the patients they discovered that 131 of them no longer wished to have the operation, 65 more replied saying they had already had the operation, 70 had moved away from their listed address, 34 had died, and a further 97 patients did not reply. From a starting-point of 950 patients, only 363 were available for operation. It was this type of story that encouraged the Secretary of State for Health, in 1984, to ask all health authorities to thoroughly review their waiting-lists. They were asked to complete this review by March 1985, but civil servants, ministers, and many in the National Health Service were disappointed to discover that the overall decrease in the waiting-lists during that period was quite small. A drop of only 1 per cent, from the September 1984 figure, in the number of non-urgent patients waiting over a year seemed a poor return for all the effort that was put into the review, particularly as some of the reduction may have been achieved by a real increase in patient throughput rather than the simple clerical review of the waiting-list. Even allowing for the fact that few health authorities had enough time to comply with the Minister's instruction, one year after his request the total list had only fallen by 3 per cent. Clearly many were disappointed that a systematic review did not produce a much greater fall in numbers. At face value, the waiting-lists did not appear to be inflated.

The failure of a centrally led drive to review waiting-lists is hardly surprising as a proper review is a very difficult and time-consuming task. One must have considerable sympathy for the medical records staff and doctors who have to devise a sensitive letter, which is effectively saying, 'Have we operated on you already, are you feeling better, have you changed your mind, have you been treated elsewhere, or are you dead?' The result of distributing such letters is to receive many enquiries and some abuse from patients and their general practitioners. When a Secretary of State sends messages down a bureaucratic chain that demands an affirmative answer it is hardly surprising that he gets one. 'Yes Minister we have reviewed the waiting-lists', says every general manager and district chairman throughout the land. The fact is that in the very waiting-lists that most require the review — that is, the very large lists which represent the bulk of the problem — the process of review is the most difficult and time-consuming. Secretaries and clerical officers, who are already under tremendous pressure because of the very long waiting-lists, are those who are required to send out the most letters, to the largest number of patients who have been on the waiting-lists for a long period of time.

My recent study of some of the country's largest waiting-lists has confirmed just how badly or incompletely some of these so-called reviews have been conducted. In each of the following cases I was assured that a waiting-list review had been conducted in 1985 or 1986.

(a) In one waiting-list of 600 orthopaedic patients, 400 of whom had waited over a year for treatment, we discovered that whilst all patients had been written to, 114 had failed to reply and the secretaries had not had the time to contact the general practitioners to discover whether the patients did indeed still require an operation.

(b) For a surgical list of over 1000 cases the administrators admitted that an unknown number of patients had declared that they no longer required to be admitted, but that their names still remained on the waiting-lists as the surgeons wished to read through the case notes and review each patient's condition before they allowed them to be crossed off the list.

(c) In an eye hospital's waiting-list of over 600 cases it was discovered that 137 of the patients should not have been recorded on the waiting-list, because the operation had actually been deferred for clinical or other reasons.

(d) One ENT waiting-list of over 4000 patients had been reviewed systematically by just two secretaries, but they had received no response from over 1000 patients, half of whom had temporary general practitioner registrations. In subsequent months they had not had the time to follow up these cases further. The patients remain on the list, even though many are unlikely to be admitted.

This type of incomplete review occurs time and time again. With these very large lists one frequently finds that over 10 per cent of the patients will never be admitted to hospital. Whilst the sceptics always criticize such reviews as being merely paper exercises, the reason for such activity is not simply clerical or political. From a practical point of view it is extremely frustrating to call patients into hospital from a waiting-list, only to discover that they no longer require the operation. Sometimes this results in the theatre sessions and the beds being wasted, even though hospitals try to have patients standing by to come in at short notice to cover those who fail to attend. A proper review of long waiting-lists will demonstrate a level of inflation that should be eliminated, not in order to artificially shorten the list, but to improve the chances of early admission for those patients who genuinely need an operation.

Lies, damned lies, and waiting-list statistics

There is a counter view which suggests that far from waiting-lists being inflated, they are actually grossly under-estimated. When

Mr Sykes, a consultant surgeon in Manchester, reviewed his hospital waiting-lists,[4] he found that large numbers of the patients admitted to his hospital were never recorded in the official waiting-list statistics. He studied 1094 patients awaiting treatment, but discovered that some were excluded because they were waiting for day-case surgery, some were excluded because they had defaulted when called for admission, and others omitted because they were awaiting clinical check or review procedures. Whilst 608 patients were on the official waiting-list, another 486 had been excluded. He suggested that the true number of patients awaiting admission to hospital was almost 80 per cent greater than the official figure. Mr Sykes forcibly pointed out some of the inadequacies of the official waiting-list statistics, although to be fair the data was specifically intended to exclude some of the categories that Mr Sykes would rather see included. Once again, it would be dangerous to argue from the specific to the general and we cannot assume that all hospitals exclude day-cases from the list in the way Mr Sykes's hospital does. Most of the hospital lists that I have studied make little or no distinction between day-cases or other forms of surgery and simply count all patients into the official statistics. There is no doubt that waiting-lists are under-estimated, but perhaps not to the extent that they are in one of Manchester's hospitals.

There is no way of knowing whether the over-estimates balance the under-estimates. The evidence clearly shows that waiting-list data is imperfect, but there is no convincing evidence which suggests that it is completely false.

Only half the story

The NHS has no systematic method of collecting data about the waiting time between seeing a general practitioner and seeing the consultant. In Fig. 3 both the patients wait for a year between seeing the general practitioner and having the operation, but their time on the hospital in-patient waiting-list is very different. One patient is on the waiting-list for 50 weeks and the other for only 5 weeks. Since the establishment of the NHS, we have only

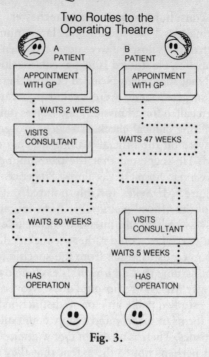

Fig. 3.

gathered information on a national level about the numbers waiting for in-patient treatment. More recently we have added information about waiting time, but only for in-patient treatment. At a local level, most health authorities collect information about the number of patients waiting and how long they wait between seeing the GP and the out-patient department. Quite often this information is distributed to general practitioners in the locality, but few authorities attempt the admittedly difficult task of providing an overall picture of the two waiting periods. Recently, after 35 years of the NHS, the first national survey of out-patient waiting time was undertaken, not by the government, not by consumer representatives, but by the British Medical Association.[5] The survey covered six specialties in 1983 and 1984 and showed that in those specialties waiting time was getting longer. It highlighted the fact that some specialties have much

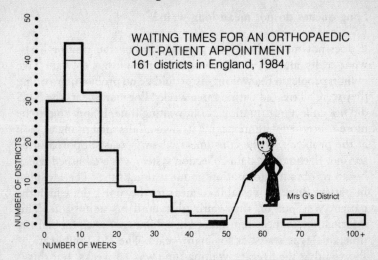

Fig. 4.

greater problems than others and also that the waiting time varies enormously from district to district. Mrs G's neighbours are indeed unfortunate to have to wait 50 weeks for an out-patient appointment to see an orthopaedic surgeon. Figure 4 shows that only seven districts in England record longer waiting times to see a consultant.

The BMA survey also laid low the myth about the balance between the two waiting times. It is sometimes suggested that the length of time spent on the in-patient list will be balanced by time spent waiting for an out-patient appointment (as shown in Fig. 3, p. 14). Some consultants prefer the policy of seeing out-patients immediately and then putting the patient on a long in-patient waiting-list, whilst others allow a long wait for an out-patient appointment and try to admit patients very quickly when they need an operation. Each system has its advantages and disadvantages. Comparing the information collected in the BMA survey with the information routinely collected about in-patient waiting time revealed that there is no obvious balancing of waiting times and a large number of districts have very severe problems for both out-patient and in-patient waiting time.

Long queues do not mean long waits?

It does not matter how many people are on the waiting-list—what really matters is how long each person has to wait. Five million people on the waiting-list would be no problem, providing they were all treated within three weeks! For many years the NHS did not collect information about waiting time. It appeared to be more concerned with managing its own affairs than trying to look at the problems of the consumers whom it was supposed to be serving. Eventually a data-collection system was established which began to obtain information about waiting time. The Hospital In-patient Enquiry was able to measure the time from which the patient was put on the waiting-list until his admission. This information has been reproduced in volumes of unhelpful 'railway timetable' type statistics for many years. The 1982 publication[6] showed that the average waiting time was 16 weeks, but this is a record of the waiting experience of those who have been admitted and tells nothing of the waiting experience of those yet to be operated on.

Since 1975 the DHSS has asked all hospitals and districts to gather information about the patients who are on their waiting-lists but have not yet been admitted. The information is divided into 'urgent' and 'non-urgent' cases. For the urgent cases, hospitals also have to specify how many have been waiting for over a month, and for the non-urgent cases how many have been waiting for over a year. It is not the most impressive of recording systems, because the decision as to what is urgent or non-urgent is left to the discretion of each consultant or his staff without any guidance or definition offered. Most consultants attempt to make a reasonable distinction, but there are a few who simply say that everything that they put on a list is urgent! Despite the imperfect data, it is abundantly obvious that for many people their time on the waiting-list can be very long. Consistently over the last ten years, a quarter of all the patients on the waiting-list have waited over a year for non-urgent treatment. The data reveals a clear pattern—the more people waiting, the more people there are who have to wait a long time.

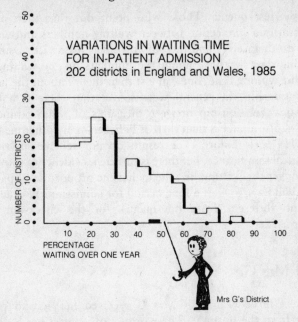

Fig. 5.

The data also confirms some of the inequality within the NHS. Mrs G and her neighbours must again count themselves as unfortunate. In the district where she is waiting for an operation, some 50 per cent of patients have waited over a year for treatment. In Fig. 5 you can see that her district is worse placed than many others, although there is one district where 85 per cent of patients wait over a year.

Now that the NHS collects some data about waiting time as well as the number waiting, we are in a position to examine more closely the theory that the two are not related. Whilst a long queue does not always mean a long wait, what do you do when you leave a supermarket? Generally speaking the number in the queue gives you a good idea about how long you will wait. When you approach the check-out do you measure the flow past each till and count the number of items in each basket, or simply go for the shortest queue? Those who point out that there is not necessarily a connection between waiting numbers and waiting time do themselves and the public a great disservice. Using the existing data we have about the numbers on the waiting-lists and the waiting time, one can test their theory about the lack of a relationship. In general we discover that there is a better statistical relationship between measures of waiting time and waiting-list numbers than there is between many other measures of NHS performance. The results do not achieve spectacular statistical significance, but there is sufficient evidence to show that the longer the waiting-list, the higher the proportion of patients who will have to wait a long period for admission. Waiting-lists are no different from the queues for the check-out at a supermarket.

And Mrs G?

After a three year wait Mrs G received her second review letter from the hospital. The wording of it upset her husband, who felt that the hospital did not want to perform the operation. He wondered if she ought to go to another hospital, but feared that this might mean a further long wait.

It would be embarrassing to try to suggest to Mrs G that waiting-lists are irrelevant and inaccurate. I do not want to tell her that her wait has probably been extended by her hospital's failure to review the list and take off patients who no longer need or want their operations. It is simply pathetic to admit that we do not know whether waiting-lists are actually larger or smaller than she might think and that they may or may not accurately measure the amount of time she is having to wait. She has long suspected the NHS is incompetent, but there is no need for me to confirm this and depress her further. She and thousands of others are in pain, and need and deserve an early operation. Merely arguing about how we measure these facts is not really helpful.

References

1. Donaldson, L., Maratos, J. I., and Richardson, R. A. (1984). Review of an orthopaedic in-patient waiting-list. *Health Trends*, **16**, 14–15.
2. Lourie, J. A. (1978). Notes on an orthopaedic waiting-list. *British Journal of Clinical Practice*, **32**, 224–5.
3. Porter, K. M. (1985). Orthopaedic audit — review of inpatient waiting lists. *British Medical Journal*, **291**, 1216–17.
4. Sykes, P. A. (1986). DHSS waiting-list statistics — a major deception? *British Medical Journal*, **293**, 1038–9.
5. Yates, J. M., and Wood, K. (1985). *Out-patient waiting time*. Inter-Authority Comparisons and Consultancy, Health Services Management Centre, Birmingham.
6. DHSS (1982). *Hospital in-patient enquiry*. Government statistical services. HMSO, London.

3

The axe and the iceberg

Waiting-lists are inevitable

The argument

It can be argued that if the NHS is going to use its resources
efficiently, a waiting-list is required in order to schedule patients
through the available theatres and beds. Thus it would be necessary
to keep some part of the existing waiting-list to achieve this
efficiency. The argument continues by suggesting that even having
allowed such scheduling, the number of patients seeking admission
always will be greater than the resources available to meet that
demand. Both the consumer and the doctor have increasing aware-
ness of what is possible and an expectation that everything should
be made available to all in need. These factors contribute to what
is seen by some as a bottomless pit of demand. Whatever the health
care services try to do, there is always more to be done. We pass on
a fable in which the demand for health care is likened to a huge
'iceberg' and the NHS is depicted as a man with an axe, chipping it
away. What little success he has at removing lumps of ice never
shows because the huge iceberg simply reveals more of its bulk
above the surface. It is difficult to find adequate measures of the
need for health care, and waiting-list numbers cannot be used for
this purpose. Waiting-lists not only under-estimate true need, but
actually help to suppress need because patients and general practitioners, both aware of the long waiting-lists, fail to refer themselves
or their patients to hospital. We do not have an accurate picture of
what level of demand exists, or precisely how much illness is held
below the surface, simply because of the very existence of long lists.
Waiting-lists have always been with us and always will be with us.

This argument holds in a stable situation, but in actual fact things are getting worse. More of us are living to a greater age than ever before and, whilst our population in Britain is not growing in size, we are gradually increasing the proportion of elderly in our population, which in turn fuels the increasing demand for health care.

The evidence

Scheduling theatre sessions

An operating theatre session usually lasts three and a half hours. Very expensive ventilating plant, complicated equipment, and a wide range of instruments have to be carefully prepared for the surgeon, his assistants, anaesthetist, nurses, theatre technicians, and a range of supporting staff, including engineers and porters. The names of the patients to be operated on have not been picked randomly, because the operating list has to allow for many factors. Are there enough available beds on the wards for the patients? Does the combined time of the operations to be performed add up to approximately three and a half hours and is there a satisfactory balance of major and minor operations, to enable junior staff to learn the full range of surgical techniques required to become a competent surgeon? Patients cannot simply be selected from the list in the order in which they arrived there. The surgeon has to make space for the most urgent cases and yet produce a balanced list. Unless theatre sessions are to be wasted, it is argued that this requires a waiting-list from which to select patients. In order to undertake such precise scheduling, surgeons would argue that they need a waiting-list of between 50 and 100 cases.

There are over 3000 surgeons in England in the five major specialties alone. If each were to have a waiting-list of 50 to 100 cases this would mean that the English waiting-list would be between 150 000 and 300 000 patients. This is between a quarter and a half of the existing waiting-list. In practice, quite a large number of surgeons work without a waiting-list and use what is called a 'booking' system. This means that the patient is seen in the out-patient clinic and offered a date for the operation. Having decided a date, the patient is booked into the diary and then attends hospital on that agreed date. Such booked cases never appear in the country's waiting-list statistics and thus add to the under-estimate of waiting-list numbers. Ignoring our failure to record these booked cases, the average waiting-list per surgical consultant is around 200 cases, but the average hides an enormous range and there are one or two surgeons who have over 2000 cases on their personal waiting-list.

The suggestion that waiting-lists are needed in order to schedule patients is not an adequate explanation of this country's waiting-lists. Scheduling can be achieved by using a booking system, but even if such a system is not used, hundreds of surgeons in this country have waiting-lists that greatly exceed the requirements for scheduling within an efficient organization. Not even the average waiting-list of 200 patients can explain why thousands of patients need to wait over a year for treatment, because most surgeons operate on over 200 waiting-list cases per year.

Never-ending demand

The demand for medical care, and in particular for surgical intervention, is absolutely enormous and has, throughout the history of the NHS, been much greater than the capacity of the health care services. Whilst additional resources may need to be put into health care in order to cope with this, demand is so great that we have to accept that it will always outstrip the supply of services. Over the last thirty years the situation has deteriorated because of tremendous scientific, technical, and medical advances that keep breaking new ground and make it possible to undertake types of surgery never previously dreamt of. Today we take hip-replacement surgery for granted and indeed we almost claim it as a right. Forty years ago surgeons could not even perform such an operation. Today the replacement of bones and joints seems almost trivial compared with the transplanting of major organs, such as hearts, lungs, and kidneys. The problem with which we are faced is what the economists call 'supply-induced demand'. The more doctors we employ, the more they investigate disease and discover new forms of treatment. In 1980 when an economist called Frost[1] analysed the trends in waiting-list statistics and compared them with the growth in the number of surgeons appointed over the same period, he found that the two appeared to be related. After a short time-lag of two or three years, a growth in the number of surgeons would be mirrored by a growth in the waiting-lists. Since Frost published that paper, hospital waiting-lists have grown more dramatically and may not be so easily explained, but there does appear to be at least some relationship between waiting-list size and the number of surgeons employed.

This is not to imply that we should blame surgeons for creating waiting-lists. They are merely taking on more and more of the 'iceberg' of medical need. Surgeons are influenced by the current state of knowledge and the availability of resources. As these two factors change they are able to alter the point at which they intervene in the progression of a disease. Sanderson[2] has described how chronic conditions gradually become more severe, starting with minor symptoms, but worsening until the point where patient and surgeon both agree surgery is necessary. The threshold of pain for individual patients and the threshold at which an operation is deemed necessary vary between patients and over time. Advances in medical science enable surgeons to intervene earlier, more speedily, or more effectively, and in pushing back the barriers they create a new demand which is soon translated into a waiting-list. Those who advance these arguments produce good evidence to show the higher levels of intervention, but seldom do they discuss the fact that the scientific and medical advances also contribute to reduced costs. New drugs and operative techniques are developed which can reduce admission rates and length of stay. These developments provide a counter-balance in the argument. Finally, there is one unpalatable feature of the 'iceberg' fable. Experts are often more interested in the new and the exciting rather than the well-established and the mundane. It is of course highly desirable to develop new techniques which will ultimately reduce morbidity, but sometimes this is done at the expense of providing a routine service. One orthopaedic surgeon who specializes in the treatment of scoliosis operates on 120 such patients each year. He also sees about ten new out-patients each week who do not suffer from this disease. They are placed on the waiting-list and never operated on.

It is not only economists and epidemiologists who are inclined to accept variations on the theme of the iceberg. Politicians have long found waiting-lists difficult to handle. Whilst political party manifestos often promise great things for the NHS, neither the Conservative nor the Labour party has got to grips with the problem. If you superimpose the colours of the Conservative and Labour governments on the graph in Fig. 1, you will find little evidence so far that either party has made any impact on waiting-lists—whatever they have said in their manifestos. Ministers of Health from both parties have often had to look back on their period of government and reflect in a somewhat fatalistic manner on their impact on waiting-lists. Enoch Powell, who was Minister of Health from 1960 to 1963 expressed the view that many of his successors must have come to share. 'I cannot but reflect sardonically on the effort I myself expended, as Minister of Health, in trying to "get the waiting lists down". It is an activity about as hopeful as filling a sieve.'[3] Powell went on to explain that regardless of ministers and their pronouncements, and action and all sorts of special efforts, the waiting-list remained at half a million people. (His book was first published in 1966, well before the waiting-list grew to three quarters of a million.) We cannot afford to be too critical of the failures of the two major political parties over the last thirty years, because we have to remember that most of us have supported one or both of them during that time. Perhaps these two political parties and all others must realize that political dogma of any sort is not going to solve the problem of hospital waiting-lists. They have failed to reduce lists, but it would be a little unfair to ask them to shoulder the full responsibility for their continued existence.

The opinions of economists, epidemiologists, and politicians are surprisingly consistent. They accept that routine waiting-list statistics are inadequate and cannot measure the demand for health care. Their intellectual arguments are powerful, but they cannot produce convincing statistical evidence. My recent survey of some of our country's larger waiting-lists produced some interesting facts which perhaps modifies the fable. It shows that waiting-lists do not consist of patients at the frontiers of medical science. The vast majority of waiting-lists are made up of patients who are requiring straightforward, uncomplicated surgery. In general surgery almost half of the patients are waiting for operations for hernias and varicose veins. In orthopaedics 10 per cent of patients await total hip replacement and at least a further 30 per cent are awaiting quite minor operations. In ophthalmology, cataract surgery dominates the waiting-list by occupying almost three quarters of the list, and in ENT, tonsils and adenoids operations constitute half of the lists. Waiting-list patients are by and large not on the frontiers of medical advancement, but are patients left behind. The reason for this may be that more urgent conditions are being treated, medicine is devoting its attention to rarer and more interesting conditions, or resources are not provided or not used to treat these common conditions.

The rising tide

An additional argument concerns the growing number of elderly people we have in the country. There is one epidemic which we can predict with some certainty—by the end of this century Great Britain will have a very much higher proportion of elderly people than it has today. Generally speaking the elderly are more prone to illness and require more frequent surgical intervention than the young. In the past thirty years the number and proportion of elderly in our population has increased and has thus put pressure on the existing resources. Most evidence suggests that our rates of treatment and intervention are increasing (e.g. there are more hospital admissions), but despite the increase

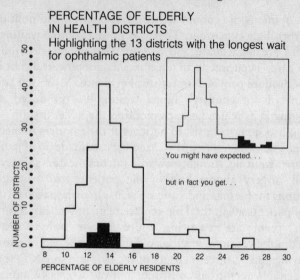

PERCENTAGE OF ELDERLY
IN HEALTH DISTRICTS
Highlighting the 13 districts with the longest wait
for ophthalmic patients

You might have expected. . .

but in fact you get. . .

NUMBER OF DISTRICTS

PERCENTAGE OF ELDERLY RESIDENTS

Fig. 6.

in tempo for all age groups not everyone requiring treatment is treated. When resources cannot cope it means that a queue has formed and all too often the elderly make up a substantial proportion of that queue—the waiting-list. This logic is borne out by our study of the patients who are on the waiting-list. Of the first 24 840 patients in our waiting-list study, 5450 (22 per cent) were aged 65 and over. The proportion of the total population who are over 65 is only 15 per cent and thus waiting-lists have a higher proportion of elderly than the rest of the population. Within the main specialties there are two which have virtually no elderly people on the waiting-list—ENT and gynaecology, but in complete contrast in opthalmology some 60 per cent of the list are 65 and over. In the two specialties with the largest number of patients waiting—general surgery and orthopaedic surgery, approximately 20 per cent of patients are over 65 years of age. This evidence seems to support the notion that the growing number of elderly will influence waiting-list numbers and also growth in waiting time.

An examination of the information at district level, however, does not support that idea. In theory those districts which have a high proportion of elderly are more likely to have a high proportion of patients waiting over a year for treatment (see the inset on Fig. 6). Given the higher demand for health care from the elderly in a specialty like ophthalmology, one might expect the larger lists and longer waits to be in the districts which have a high proportion of elderly. The actual data in Figure 6 does not support that theory. There is no statistically significant relationship between the length of waiting time and the proportion of elderly in ophthalmology, nor indeed in any other surgical specialty.

And Mrs G?

The arguments about inevitability are quite depressing. It is no good me telling Mrs G that her wait of over five years has been necessary in order to make best use of hospital resources. That might be a satisfactory explanation for those who wait for a short period or time, but over 132 000 people like Mrs G in England and Wales have had to wait over a year for treatment already.

Intellectually Mrs G can understand the argument about the iceberg, but she does find it difficult to understand why a problem which affects most Western countries leaves Great Britain with a waiting-list, whilst most of its neighbours have no such list. She wonders whether the British are more honest in collecting data, or less effective in managing health services. The iceberg theory may explain a waiting-list of three quarters of a million, but it does not explain why waiting time is very long in one district and much shorter in another. Patients who are waiting for relatively minor operations might be forgiven for thinking that the NHS is attempting to melt the iceberg from underneath the water. The large tip of the iceberg is clear for all to see, yet it seems to be ignored. How long will Mrs G have to sit on top of the iceberg whilst her surgeon keeps diving under the surface?

References

1. Frost, C. E. B. (1980). Surgical waiting-lists: an economist's view. In *Waiting for hospital treatment*. Harrogate Seminar Report, DHSS.
2. Sanderson, H. F. (1982). What is a waiting-list? *British Medical Journal*, **285**, 1368–9.
3. Powell, J. E. (1976). *Medicine and politics: 1975 and after*. Pitman Medical.

4

Money, money, money

Waiting-lists are caused by under-funding

The argument

It is claimed that if the NHS was given more resources the current long waiting-lists would either be reduced or eliminated. The argument comes in two parts. Firstly, it is suggested that by comparison with other countries we do not give sufficient money to our health care services. The second argument is a straight-forward demonstration that there is existing need for which there are known cures and thus that increased provision will reduce the need. One of the strongest lobbies for the NHS is the staff who work in it. Whilst different groups of staff will argue with each other about all kinds of issues in the NHS, there is one place where unions and professional groups of all sorts will stand side by side. All agree that we need more money. Enoch Powell[1] observed that the one thing any Minister of Health will have to get used to is 'the continual deafening chorus of complaint which rises day and night from every part of it' . . . for more money. One recent example of harmony came from the British Medical Association, the Royal College of Nurses and the Institute of Health Services Management[2] which forced a government minister to admit that 2 per cent a year increase in real expenditure for the next three years was needed by the NHS.[3]

Those who put forward these arguments are sometimes optimistic and express the view that additional cash will actually eliminate waiting-lists. Others, perhaps more realistically, merely claim that additional cash will help us eat further into the iceberg of demand and thus significantly reduce waiting-lists. In the latter case it is argued the waiting-list still includes far too many people who are in danger of dying on the waiting-list or, who are in pain and living a restricted life-style. It is that element of the waiting-list that we would seek to attack with additional resources.

The evidence

International comparisons

In making comparisons between countries it is traditional to study what proportion of the nation's wealth (the gross national product) is spent on health. The United States of America, for example, 'spends almost 10% of its GNP on health care and yet cannot guarantee the universal coverage and access to care that Britain provides for its people with less than 6% of its GNP.'[4] We keep telling ourselves that we have a National Health Service that is the envy of the world. Value, pound for pound, probably suggests that it is, but in recent years other countries have overtaken us in the health league tables. For the conventional measures of death rates, life expectancy, and morbidity our improvements have been less than in other countries and we therefore begin to slip back in comparison. Looking at the proportion of the GNP (gross national product) spent on health care, we find that although we have consistently increased the proportion of our GNP spent on health in the past twenty years, other European countries are frequently spending more than we do and their increases are often at a greater rate.[5,6] It is a fair criticism to say that Great Britain does not spend as much of its GNP on health care as many other developed nations, but it must also be recognized that there are many countries who spend less and yet do not have a waiting-list.

Internal comparisons

Not only are there differences in the amount of money spent on health care by nations, there are also large differences in how much money is spent on hospital care in different parts of Britain. When the NHS was set up in 1948 it was apparent that resources were not evenly distributed. The provision of hospital services had developed haphazardly in response to local demand, the work of charities and the differing attitudes of local authorities. As there was no national organization, there was no national plan. Once the NHS had been established, all that was changed. Regional Hospital Boards were created with responsibility to plan the development of hospital services throughout their region and for over thirty-five years they have been responsible for planning hospital specialist services for each locality. During these years the pattern has changed in each country, but currently, English health care is divided between 191 districts with an average population of about a quarter of a million people. This means that each district serves either a major town and its hinterland, a large rural area covering a number of smaller towns and villages, or a portion of a large city. The regional authorities plan and provide the hospital and community services for each locality. Let us first examine how successful they have been in the distribution of beds and some of the other resources required to run a surgical service and then see what effect the distribution has on the size and length of waiting-lists.

(a) The distribution of hospital beds

Currently the provision of hospital beds for the specialties of general surgery and urology can vary between 2 and 17 beds per 10 000 population per district. How can we explain such a wide variation from district to district, particularly as one would assume that general surgical and urological problems would not differ greatly from one part of the country to another? Firstly, some of the boundaries between health districts are very artificial and if a district general hospital is situated on the boundary it would not be surprising if it drew many of its patients from the neighbouring district, simply because they find that it is easier to get to. Most districts tend to treat some patients from outside their district and this is particularly so in the case of urban districts where it is very difficult to draw boundaries which take account of bus, train, and car communications. Secondly, it has been a

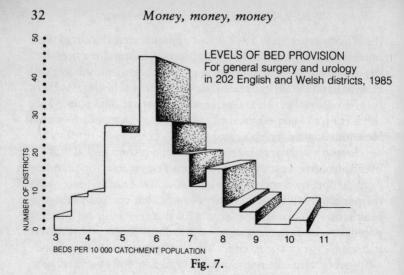

Fig. 7.

fundamental principle in the NHS that patients can go wherever they wish for treatment and their general practitioner can refer them to any district that he thinks appropriate. Boundaries on the map should never be boundaries to treatment. A third reason for 'cross-boundary' flow is that not all districts can provide a completely full service within each specialty. There are occasions when certain surgeons will develop and perfect particular types of operation and knowing this the general practitioner will refer certain of his patients to a neighbouring district rather than to his own locality.

It is for these types of reasons that it is unfair to measure the success of regional authorities in allocating beds simply by relating the beds to the resident population. One needs to take account of the flow of patients across these boundaries. Whilst statisticians have yet to find a method which measures this flow accurately, Fig. 7 does show the best available results of various methods of trying to take account of cross-boundary flow. It shows that the beds provided in relation to the population served can range from 3 beds per 10 000 population to almost 11 beds per 10 000 population. Even allowing for cross-boundary flow and despite thirty-five years of a national health service trying to balance our peculiar historical inheritance, we still have more than a three-fold variation in the provision of beds in English districts. It would be comforting to think that such a wide variation could be explained by different needs in the community. Perhaps the districts at the far right-hand side of Fig. 7 have a higher proportion of elderly patients, greater levels of morbidity in the community, poor housing and other socio-economic problems, or low levels of general practice and primary care. Unfortunately, none of these reasons have ever been shown to explain the variation adequately. All the evidence points to the fact that history and politics are stronger influences on planning than current need or equity.

(b) The distribution of other resources

For years our examination of resources in the health service has concentrated on looking at beds, but managing a good surgical service requires many other elements, such as surgeons, theatres, out-patient clinics, and other supporting facilities and staff. There is no evidence in any of these fields that we do any better in balancing these other resources than we do with beds. The number of hospital doctors (i.e. consultants, senior registrars, and registrars) provided for general surgery and urology in relation to the population served, can vary from just over 1 per 100 000 population to over 10 doctors for the same size of population—a tenfold difference in a nationalized service! Seldom do we find other resources such as out-patient clinics, operating theatres, nurses, and support staff quite so badly distributed, but equality of distribution leaves much to be desired. Despite years of effort to re-allocate resources, we still find three to tenfold variations in resource provision with the north–south divide causing as much argument in health care as it does in other fields.

(c) Do the variations in allocation explain the variation in waiting-lists?

The complexity of resource allocation is confused by the fact that these variations are not consistent. They are not necessarily

LONG WAITS AND A SHORTAGE OF RESOURCES
Highlighting 21 of the 200 districts in England
and Wales for general surgery and urology, 1985

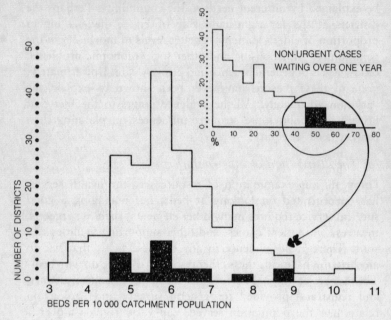

NON-URGENT CASES
WAITING OVER ONE YEAR

Fig. 8.

consistent between specialties and thus a district deprived of
resources for general surgery may not be so deprived for trauma
and orthopaedics. Nor is the allocation consistent within
specialties, leaving some districts well provided for beds, but with
too few theatres. Throughout the country the complexity of the
balancing act leaves some districts woefully short of resources in
all quarters, some under-provided for one or two key components
and others relatively well-blessed. As most districts can point out
some shortage, virtually all can claim that the poor distribution
and balance of resources between towns, hospitals, and specialties
adversely affects their attempts to reduce hospital waiting-lists.

Given this, one might expect to see that the long waiting-lists in England and Wales are to be found in those districts where the most severe shortages occur. Figure 8 identifies the 21 districts with the worst waiting experience in general surgery and urology and then superimposes those same districts on the allocation of beds (first illustrated in Fig. 7). It shows that there is no obvious relationship between a shortage of beds and long waiting time. One of the possible explanations for this is that the long waiting-lists occur not in the district that is short of resources, but in the neighbouring districts which have to compensate for those neighbours who are actually short of resources. It is an interesting theory, but there is no evidence to support it. Our recent study of some of the worst waiting-lists in the country in 1986 showed that three quarters of the waiting-lists were made up of people from the local district and in the majority of districts the proportion was much higher. Only in a few cases were there examples of large waiting-lists being caused by an inflow of patients from neighbouring districts.

It is possible to look at other measures of waiting-lists and waiting time and compare them with bed, surgeon, or theatre provision, but which ever measures are used, no convincing relationship can be established. Either the data is too poor to be used, or one has to conclude that the provision of resources at district level explains very little about the varying length of hospital waiting-lists.

And Mrs G?

The evidence about our relative shortage of resources compared with the rest of Europe is quite impressive. I could blame successive governments for failing to increase the funding for our National Health Service, because a waiting-list of almost three quarters of a million seems to fit quite neatly with the claim of shortage of resources. If I am to be honest though, I have two problems. The first difficulty is that Mrs G and I will have to be realistic when we ask for more cash. More for the NHS will mean less for someone else. We may have to take part in debates about the means of reducing expenditure elsewhere. If we believe that money should be transferred from defence then we shall have to join in the debate about the reduction in conventional or nuclear fire power. If we think that operating on the sick is of more importance than spending money on opera and theatre, then we must join in the debate about reducing expenditure on the arts and deciding which theatres are to close. Shutting Drury Lane theatre to provide the resources to build an operating theatre near to Mrs G seems a long and improbable route. Training a nuclear technician to become a theatre technician is also a long route. It might help Mrs G's grandchildren, but a more immediate solution seems necessary.

My second difficulty is that the shortage of resources argument does not explain the variation in the size of waiting-lists from district to district throughout Britain. I know that Mrs G's district is not short of surgeons and I know that it has a better provision of beds than virtually any other district in the country. It is true that it is short of theatre space in the particular hospital to which she is hoping to be admitted, but I also know that other theatres in the same district are not fully used. It is not too easy to explain that a shortage of resources is the reason for Mrs G's long wait.

References

1. Powell, J. E. (1976). *Medicine and politics: 1975 and after*. Pitman Medical, London.
2. Maynard, A. and Bosanquet, N. (1986). *Public expenditure on the NHS: recent trends and future problems*. Report commissioned by the Institute of Health Services Management, the British Medical Association, and the Royal College of Nursing.
3. BMA News Review, (1986). Minister admits NHS needs 2 per cent annual growth. *BMA News Review*, **12**, 11.
4. Torrens, P. R. (1982). Some potential hazards of unplanned expansion of private health insurance in Britain. *Lancet*, **1**, 29–31.

5. Maynard, A. (1975). *Health care in the European Community*. Croom Helm, London.

6. Parkin, D., McGuire, A., and Yule, B. (1986). *International comparisons of expenditure on health care and its relationship to national income: a critique and some new evidence*. Discussion paper no. 03/86, Health Economics Research Unit, University of Aberdeen.

5

The corpulent bureaucrat

Waiting-lists are caused by inefficiency

The argument

Critics of the NHS argue that it does not make efficient use of the resources that it has and consequently waiting-lists could be reduced considerably, simply by improving efficiency. It is, of course, very easy to criticize the way an organization works. Many who have spent the best part of their working life in the NHS are proud of it and are quite naturally defensive when it is criticized. Having spent twenty years working in the NHS, it always irks me when someone from the CBI or elsewhere in commerce and industry complains about inefficiency. I always think back to my early days as a trainee in NHS management when I was given an industrial attachment. I spent a week looking around some Lancashire cotton mills seeing how they were managed. The company I had joined had recently taken over one of its competitors and the two were based in the same old-fashioned office block near the centre of Manchester. The larger firm, which I had never heard of, had a very modern set-up, with the latest office machinery and computerized invoicing. Two floors below it was the head office of the firm it was taking over. It was a very famous name in clothing manufacture and it had an accounts department that resembled descriptions one reads in some of Dickens's novels. Although it was the early sixties, senior clerks sat on high stools at desks supervising dozens of other clerks who were writing out by hand five copies of every invoice. Even the health service had heard of carbon paper! Like many others I am not impressed by the efficiency in some parts of commerce and industry. Today when the health service is encouraged to learn some lessons from the free market, one is sarcastically inclined to say, 'If they are so clever, why is Britain in its current economic plight?'

Those who wish to compare the NHS unfavourably with industry and commerce, must realize that the NHS is one of the largest employers in Western Europe and its size and complexity is quite awesome compared with many commercial and industrial concerns that other employers have to manage. The managing director of the NHS has a budget of over £12 350 000 000 and a staff of over 800 000 people, who during the course of each year contact over eight million of the inhabitants of the country. Many English districts have more staff and a larger budget than the Dunlop empire, once run by one of Britain's top managers, Sir Michael Edwards. Would he have been prepared to manage an English health district and earn between £20 000 and £30 000 per annum? If the NHS is inefficient, criticisms need to be set against that background. Its resources are predominantly people and its working material consists solely of people. As people make errors the NHS can never be perfect. In human organizations, inefficiency is guaranteed.

Readers will detect the defensive bias of a man who has spent over twenty years working in the NHS! Like all other NHS staff, I feel that both industrialists and consumer organizations share a considerable ignorance of how the system works, which means that they do not understand the problems. What I have to admit, however, is that the extent and level of inefficiency is actually greater than they think. For almost forty years the managers of the NHS and the medical profession have failed to get to grips with widespread, but not total, inefficiency in the use of beds, theatres, and surgical staff. The bias of this chapter is not one of defensiveness, but of an 'inside' informer.

The evidence

Three of the principle components of an effective surgical service are hospital beds, operating theatres, and surgeons. It should not be necessary to emphasize that there are many other vital components, but in a book of this size I propose to examine each of these three elements in some detail and comment on the problems of balancing them.

Empty beds?

Hotels and aircraft are not always fully booked and any organization needs some spare capacity in order to run efficiently. Clearly, one cannot expect the NHS to use every hospital bed every day, but it seems an incredible paradox that we should have 50 000 acute beds empty each day, whilst over half a million people are waiting for treatment. It may be argued that 25 per cent spare capacity, which is the average for England and Wales, is a reasonable level, but when we come to examine performance district by district we soon see that there is an enormous amount of variation. Figure 9 shows the percentage of empty beds in English health districts in three surgical specialties. One cannot immediately use this as an index of efficiency, as one would hardly suggest that a district that only has 5 per cent of beds empty is necessarily being efficient. It may be forced into that position because of a terrible shortage of beds, or patients may be kept in for an unnecessarily long period of time, thus filling their beds needlessly. In either event enormous pressure is placed on the ward staff, who are faced with a very short time period between one discharge and the next admission. When the gap between patients is very short it quite often means that emergency admissions have to be deflected to other locations. Districts performing on the left-hand side of these diagrams therefore, cannot automatically be considered efficient. On the right-hand side of the diagram, however, one can see that there are some districts where some specialties have over 50 per cent of the beds unused.

There are all kinds of reasons that could explain this apparent waste of resources. Maybe there are not enough surgeons, nurses, or theatres, or the district is unable to balance its resources and thus the beds have to lie empty. To some extent that is quite a reasonable explanation, but if it goes on year after year, one has

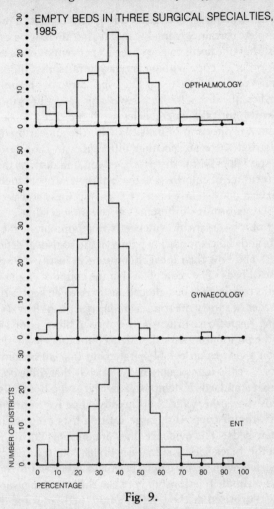

Fig. 9.

to realize that the authority is effectively staffing empty beds and wasting an enormous amount of revenue each year because it fails to balance its resources. The second argument for having a high proportion of empty beds is that they are needed in order to cope with the variation in emergency admission patterns. It is of course true that the demand for emergency admissions cannot be predicted with complete certainty from day to day, but there is no evidence to suggest that one needs to keep over 25 per cent of one's capacity empty in order to cope with emergency admissions. Indeed, it is interesting to note that in the specialty of trauma and orthopaedics, the districts which have large specialist orthopaedic units that do not take emergencies at all are often those which waste a high proportion of beds. As with the allocation of beds, one finds that there are peculiar differences in the use of beds between specialties within districts. One can find districts that have a low percentage of emptiness in most of their surgical specialties, others have a consistently high level of emptiness and yet others that display enormous differences between specialties.

This type of statistical evidence is not popular in the NHS. Managers and clinicians quickly point out the statistical deficiencies in the data and how their local circumstances justify the apparent under-use of beds. They complain that the count of empty beds at midnight is unfair, that bed allocations have to be kept artificially high in order to satisfy the training requirements of Royal College or nursing inspectors. In truth, they are making poor excuses. Neither the national statistical evidence, nor the anecdotes about Mr Tebbit's visit to an eye hospital claim that all hospitals and specialties have too many empty beds—merely that some do. By the NHS's own standards it demonstrates that some hospitals waste more beds than others and that there is scope for improvement.

Perhaps the districts with large waiting-lists are those which waste their beds? The evidence does not support such a theory. Amongst the 'black spot' waiting-lists of this country, one can find some districts with many empty beds and others with very few. There is no simple relationship between these two measures, but one is left surprised at the level of empty beds in some districts which have large waiting-lists.

Wasted theatres?

One of the rather strange features of data collection in the NHS is, that for well over thirty years, we have failed to collect data

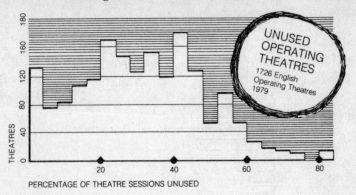

PERCENTAGE OF THEATRE SESSIONS UNUSED

Fig. 10.

about operating-theatres systematically. It is true that every theatre
has a register which accurately records details about each patient
and the operation undertaken, but in the vast majority of hospitals
that data has not been collected together to form the basis of any
returns to district, region, or the Department of Health. Hospital
Activity Analysis data could provide an analysis of operations,
but unfortunately this would be rather ineffective as its data is
based on individual patients. Thus, from this source it would not
be easy to gather together information about what happens in any
particular theatre or operation list. This major deficiency will be
corrected when the recommendations of the Körner Report[1] are
implemented, but in the meantime evidence about the use of
operating-theatres relies on special surveys that have been carried
out. One of the largest surveys ever undertaken about operating-
theatres was by the Medical Architectural Research Unit.[2] Its
survey showed the proportion of theatre sessions that were unused
in 1979 (see Fig. 10). Many other surveys of theatre usage have
been undertaken, although most of them have been concerned
with smaller numbers of operating-theatres. The Oxford Regional
Health Authority has undertaken two or three very systematic
reviews of theatre usage. The published information from one of
their surveys[3] admits quite openly that, 'facts clearly show that

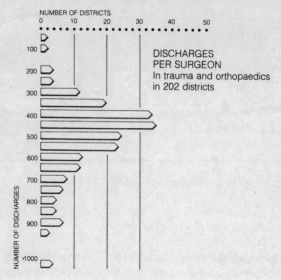

Fig. 11.

some scope exists for making greater use of the available resources'. At the moment, there are no surveys that link theatre utilization and bed use on a national level, but the recent production of performance indicators by the Department of Health does illustrate the very wide range of theatre sessions available in relation to bed provision. There is ample evidence that many hospitals throughout this country do not make full use of the operating theatre sessions available.

One of the surprising features from our detailed study of some of the worst waiting-lists is how infrequently physical theatre capacity is a problem. So far, in only two cases have I found it necessary to support the need to build additional theatres. What is far more common is the inability of the district to staff and fund all the available theatre sessions. This leads to some hideous paradoxes and in at least three English cities over 1000 patients await cataract surgery, whilst ophthalmic theatres lie unused, in some cases for over half of the week. Although this might seem evidence of under-funding, these theatres have lain unused for years during a period when revenue has increased. The efficient use of theatres is not a strong point in some districts of the NHS!

Under-used surgeons?

The work-load of surgical teams varies. One would expect it to do so, because teams are quite often of a different size (some consultants are supported by a senior registrar and others are not) and teams undertake different types of work-load (e.g. some general surgeons undertake urological work, whilst others leave it to consultant urologists, and some orthopaedic surgeons operate on scoliosis patients whilst others do not). Even allowing for differences in case mix, when we standardize the number of patients treated by surgeons (registrars, senior registrars, and consultants), we find there are enormous differences in work-load between districts. Figure 11 shows that there are some districts where orthopaedic surgeons treat 200 cases per annum and in others over 1000. When you remember that not all patients require an operation, it will be appreciated that the range of operations per surgeon is from less than 150 to over 750 operations. In some districts at the extremes of this distribution I have examined the theatre registers and counted the annual number of operations for each surgeon, both senior and junior. I have found no evidence that differences in case mix explain the enormous variations between the work-load per surgeon. At the bottom of the distribution, in Fig. 11, there are consultant surgeons who do over 500 operations per annum, but at the top of the diagram surgeons do less than 150 operations per annum. This latter group are undertaking about three operations a week per full-time or maximum part-time NHS surgeon. One would be happier if this low work-load could be explained by a compensating heavy work-load in other areas, such as examining for royal colleges, undertaking research work, teaching junior medical staff or involvement in the management of the NHS, but unfortunately, this is seldom the case. One should not necessarily assume that this is merely because the surgeons themselves are unwilling to operate—I have found examples of surgeons who have only been given one or two operating sessions per week, despite being on a full-time or maximum part-time contract. Whilst there are many surgeons who work extremely long hours, there is undoubtedly a proportion of surgeons in this country who could undertake more operating.

The imperfections of NHS data cannot hide the fact that work rates vary enormously and that some improvement is possible. The bureaucracy of the NHS and those professional groups that advise it tends to avoid challenging working practices. Given the particular problem of a large cataract waiting-list, I was surprised to find ophthalmic surgeons operating only two half-days a week. Their Faculty advises this rate of operating and yet with the co-operation of some surgeons we were able to secure a temporary 50 per cent increase in operating, simply by each surgeon doing one more list per week. Given that most surgeons in all specialties enjoy operating, it is surprising that the NHS allows some surgeons to operate so infrequently.

Are the large lists to be found in districts where the surgeons operate less? Once again the evidence is inconclusive. Some are and some are not. There is no simple relationship between the two factors, but one is left with an uneasy feeling about districts where there are long lists and relatively under-used surgeons. Could they not do better?

The difficult balancing act

Running a complex organization like a hospital is not easy. You might argue that it would be most surprising if every hospital managed to make full use of its beds, theatres, and surgeons. It may be that the districts which have a high proportion of empty beds are actually using their surgeons and theatres to the limit. It may be that districts with a high proportion of empty theatres are nevertheless using their surgeons to the limit and keeping their beds full. It may be that in those districts where surgeons are doing a very limited work-load they are nevertheless using every available bed and theatre. It may be that the districts in which resources are wasted have no waiting-list problems. It is also possible that Scunthorpe will win the FA cup next season!

Whatever complex statistical analyses are made of the available data, there is no evidence so far that the inefficiencies in one element are balanced by the maximum use of all other elements.

And Mrs G?

It would be difficult to deny to Mrs G that the NHS is inefficient. Her NHS—the local district in which she awaits treatment—is seen by her to be inefficient, simply because it does not deliver the goods for her or 2000 others on the same list. I could try to persuade her that the evidence suggests that inefficiency does exist, but that there is no proof that it causes waiting-lists. She would probably be polite enough to accept my argument—providing I did not admit that I knew one or two unsavoury facts about her district—it has a high proportion of unused beds, the surgeons concerned undertake a relatively low number of operations, and in some of the district's theatres there is unused capacity (not to mention a temporary portable theatre lying unused). Whilst the statistical evidence does not neatly link large lists with the simple measures of inefficiency, there are many districts where large lists and long waits accompany an inefficient organization.

References

1. Körner, E. (1981). *A report of the working groups A to the steering group on health services information*. Körner Report.
2. Medical Architecture Research Unit (1981). *An Evaluation of the provision and utilisation of operating theatre suites*. Summary report, DHSS Commission No.W74/SD/385A, The Polytechnic of North London.
3. Barr, A., McNeilly, R. H., and Rogers, S. (1982). Use of operating theatres. *British Medical Journal*, **285**, 1059–61.

6

The hypocritical oath

Waiting-lists are caused by selfishness

The argument

So far the explanations offered for long waiting-lists have
been 'impersonal'. Blame has been laid at the door of imperfect
data, advances in technology, the increasing number of elderly,
successive governments, and incompetent bureaucracy. All these
targets are difficult to pin down and individuals are not
identified. The argument advanced here is more personal and
thus perhaps more sinister. It suggests that staff use waiting-lists
to further their own ends—that patients suffer for the selfishness
of staff. Such criticism appears harsh, as Health Service staff have
a long tradition of upholding the aspirations of Hippocrates,
the fifth-century Greek physician, and Florence Nightingale,
the founder of modern-day nursing. Both emphasized the need
for staff to do their best for their patients. The accusation,
however, is made that some actions have more to do with
hypocracy than Hippocrates and that industrial action and private
practice are both undertaken for the benefit of the staff,
rather than for the benefit of patients. The counter argument is
that industrial action is justified on the grounds that ultimately
the patient will benefit and that private medicine provides
additional care and thus supports the hard pressed NHS. The
private practice argument is one of the most controversial issues
in health care and by far the most contentious issue in regard to
waiting-lists. Private medicine enables those who can afford it,
to avoid NHS queues. Those who cannot afford it have to wait
longer.

Long NHS waiting-lists and a private medical system which enables such queues to be jumped can cause painful dilemmas for both the surgeon and the patient. Frequently both will consider what alternatives are available to them. Often it is the patient who raises the question of private care. One patient felt he could not wait seven days for an out-patient appointment for a consultation about an abscess in his back passage. He obtained a private consultation and when the consultant recommended admission the patient asked, 'Would there be any advantage in going privately?' 'No', replied the consultant, who immediately arranged for his emergency admission to an NHS hospital where his junior staff successfully undertook the necessary operation.

On many occasions the issues are not so simple. When the condition does not require urgent attention and there is a long wait the consultant can, if asked, describe how precisely the same treatment can be obtained privately and at what approximate cost. The dilemma for the patient is quite simple — can he afford it? The surgeon has two dilemmas. Firstly, he can be seen to lead the conversation towards the subject of private care and thus be accused of using the situation to his own advantage. Secondly, he is part of an organization (the NHS) which is failing to cope with demand. Whilst he can legitimately claim that he cannot be held responsible for all NHS inefficiency and the nation's failure to provide adequate resources, he is nevertheless part of that system. He shares some of the responsibility for failing to organize efficiently and for failing to convince the government to provide adequate resources. He is in the difficult position where he can be accused of not trying hard enough or even of manipulating the system for his own ends. The consultant is in a strange system which actually provides him with a financial incentive for not running a well organized NHS service. He has a financial incentive to be inefficient.

The evidence

Industrial action

Earlier in this book (Fig. 1) we saw that waiting-lists had remained at around half a million for twenty years, but during the 1970s

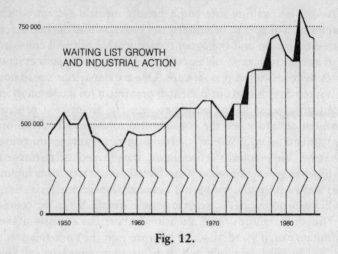

Fig. 12.

and early 1980s jumped to three quarters of a million. Most of the increase occurred in the four years 1973, 1975, 1978, and 1982 (see Fig. 12). In three of those years there were some of the worst confrontations seen in the NHS. In 1973 the first major strike of ancillary staff took place. In 1975 consultants and juniors took action in the form of a work-to-rule and in 1982 there was further widespread industrial action by ancillary staff. The 1978 jump in waiting-lists is not so easily explained. Quarterly waiting-list figures show that throughout 1976, 1977, and most of 1978 the waiting-list in England remained steady at 600 000. There was then a very sudden jump between 30 September and 31 December 1978, which continued rising up to March 1979 and this second large jump of well over 70 000 cases coincided with yet another outburst of industrial action by ancillary staff. The particular action was intended to affect planned admissions from the waiting-list. When the dispute was settled in April 1979 admissions returned to normal and by the end of 1979 waiting-lists had started to reduce. The only major rise in waiting-lists that does not coincide precisely with staff industrial action is the jump of over 50 000 that occurred between September and December 1978. It may be that there is some other factor that can explain this rise, but the most likely explanation merely points back to industrial action. It is possible that the administrative and clerical staff whose work was disrupted by the industrial action of others were unable to complete their annual waiting-list returns as close to 31 December as they would normally do. Given that one cannot retrospectively fill in returns that demand a physical count of waiting-list cards, perhaps this count was undertaken by some hospitals in the beginning of 1979 when waiting-lists had risen. Whatever the explanation for that particular quirk, it does not alter the fact that most of the major growth periods in hospital waiting-lists coincide with industrial action.

There can be little doubt that industrial action severely affects the running of the NHS—that is what it is intended to do. Whilst staff and government argue patients suffer.

Private practice

As this subject is so controversial it is important to emphasize that this chapter sets out to examine the evidence about how the current system fails. There are many who are opposed to the current system and opinion ranges from the total abolition of private medicine to the total abolition of state medicine. Before examining the defects of the current system it might be useful to clarify precisely how that system works. This next section is designed mainly for those readers who are unfamiliar with the workings of the NHS and the private sector.

How it works

Britain has a National Health Service which provides virtually free treatment for all its citizens. I use the word 'virtually' because some charges are made for certain prescriptions, mainly for medicines and spectacles. Clearly the service is not 'free' in that it is paid for mainly from taxes, but at the time when the patient needs treatment, particularly the very expensive elements like admission to hospital, it is free. The state service, however, is not a total monopoly and any citizen can choose to ignore the NHS and see a consultant privately. This is done either by making direct contact with a consultant, or more usually, by asking the advice of his or her NHS general practitioner in choosing an appropriate consultant. Patients choose to go privately for a number of reasons.

1. They can specify precisely by which physician or surgeon they wish to be treated and rest assured that investigations and operations will be carried out by their chosen consultant.

2. Private care usually means that the patient can arrange precisely when he is to be admitted. For those with business commitments, or simply a busy work and social life this is very attractive.

3. Private consultation and admission can mean superior accommodation and facilities. This is not universally the case, as there are some poor private consulting rooms and old private hospitals which are inferior to newly built NHS hospitals, but as a general rule private care offers some extras. These often include private rooms, sole use of telephone and television, superior furnishing and fittings, and a greater choice of menu.

4. Private care means an earlier consultation as an out-patient and speedier admission to hospital, particularly for an operation. This is generally the most important incentive to 'go privately' and it is the first reason given by BUPA and others in their advertising material. Private patients avoid NHS queues.

Private treatment is paid for by the patient, at or near the time of consultation, either directly by the patient or through the patient's private insurance. There are two elements to the payment. There is the fee to the consultant in respect of the consultation and any treatment or operation undertaken. Where admission is necessary there are also the charges made by the hospital. Private patients can be admitted to private hospitals, or to the limited number of private beds in NHS hospitals. In the case of the NHS, charges are meant to cover the cost of hospital care rather than to be profit-making.

The number of private hospitals is growing, as is the proportion of people who insure for private medical care. Whilst there is a certain lack of consistency in collecting information about private health care, it would appear that in 1984 there were some 207 private hospitals with about 12 800 beds. Not all of these hospitals can take surgical cases and it is estimated that there are about 8100 beds in those private hospitals which are equipped with operating-theatres. In 1984 the number of private beds in NHS hospitals stood at about 3000. Despite the growth in the past ten years, the proportion of private beds is still less than 10 per cent of all acute hospital beds. Three out of every four private patients are insured with a commercial company or a provident association. About 90 per cent of all insurance is provided by three associations—the Western Provident Association, Private Patients Plan, and British United Provident Association. The proportion of the population insured grew from 4 per cent in 1973 to 7½ per cent in 1982. Very many people are insured through their employers rather than personal insurance.

Private medical care is undertaken almost exclusively by consultants who will initially have received their training in the NHS, starting in medical school and going through all the training grades until appointed as a consultant. During training they receive no remuneration for private practice. Once a doctor is fully trained and appointed as a consultant he can work for the NHS and at the same time undertake private practice. He is entitled to receive a full-time salary which rises from £23 000 to £30 340 per annum, providing his income from private practice does not exceed 10 per cent of his salary. Once his private earnings exceed the 10 per cent figure his contract is reduced to a 'ten-elevenths' part-time contract. Consultants are expected to give substantially the same service and time to the NHS as would have been done in a whole-time appointment. Traditionally consultants contracts are expressed in elevenths, based on the notion of half-days in a five-and-a-half-day week. Each eleventh is called a session and notionally is considered to be three and a half hours. There are no regulations about consultants earnings in private practice and I can find no recently published data about income. BUPA has a scale of recommended fees for operations. In May 1984 a major operation such as hysterectomy had a recommended fee for the surgeon of £500. Intermediate operations like tonsillectomy were £285, and minor operations, such as draining a breast abscess, £145. Major plus operations like hip replacement cost £615 and more complex major surgery from £855 to £1720. All these charges are automatically higher in the London area.

Private care has the obvious advantage, for those who can afford it, of saving time and it offers a financial advantage to consultants and private companies who make a profit out of private medicine.It is also claimed that the private sector is of benefit to the NHS because it relieves the NHS of a considerable work-load that currently is not being undertaken. On the basis that the NHS is run efficiently and that private work is only undertaken in non-NHS time, the claim is powerful.

How it doesn't work

All human endeavour is subject to human failings and the health care system is no exception. Virtually every part of any system can be abused and no one can pretend that failings do not occur. There are a whole host of petty 'fiddles', but the most serious allegations concern, firstly, the exploitation of patients by using the long waiting time to force them into private medical care and secondly, the failure to fulfil contractual obligations. Few people dispute the fact that such abuse occurs. The argument is about the extent of such abuse. In examining the evidence we need to keep a sense of proportion. This country has a very large number of incredibly hard-working and honest surgeons. They are in the majority and it is they who are the first to acknowledge that their profession's reputation is scarred by the action of some of their colleagues.[1] All surgeons in the NHS work in an environment that provides too little incentive for hard work in that service. The salary offered seems ludicrous beside some of those available in commerce. In gathering the material for this book I kept a cutting about a chief executive who had a salary rise of £175 000. His salary of £275 000 would buy nine consultant surgeons in the NHS. As I complete the manuscript of this book the same gentleman hit the headlines when he resigned his post during an investigation into the mishandling of share dealings.

The NHS does not provide such spectacular examples of the mishandling of money. Its problems pale into financial insignificance compared with share dealing, but even highly trained and very skilful medical and surgical staff are human and some of them will 'fiddle' their travelling expenses and bend financial systems to their own advantage. The stories of such petty abuse are legion:

- asking for cash for consultation and operation fees in order to avoid paying tax;

- making sure that theatre sister's off-duty is arranged so that she is always available to assist in operations at the nearby private hospital;

- borrowing instruments from the NHS without permission in order to operate in the private hospital;

- stealing hip prostheses from the NHS;

- not declaring private patient fees to the NHS or to tax authorities.

There are many stories of this nature and they are treated as part of NHS folklore. The ones mentioned could have all occurred in one hospital in one year and there would be no reason to believe that that hospital was unique. Anecdotes do not provide adequate evidence, but in recent years the work of DHSS auditors, the police, and the Director of Public Prosecutions has provided evidence that fraud does exist. For doctors to claim that it is because of administrative and systems failures is ludicrous. Ignorance of the law is no defence, not even for a doctor. Whilst there is clear evidence of fraud, I believe that on the whole it is relatively minor. I do not condone it, but it has a less direct effect on patients than the more major issues which follow.

Exploiting waiting (for an out-patient appointment)

For many people private practice is first considered when they hear how long they have to wait before they can see a consultant. Typically the problem presents itself as follows. An 84-year-old lady goes to see her general practitioner because she had been suffering from a severe pain in her right foot for some weeks. The general practitioner feels that she should be referred to an orthopaedic surgeon, and makes an appointment for her—in ten months' time. Such a case is not normal, but it is typical. Waiting time for out-patients can be extremely long and varies enormously across England. The thought of such a long wait makes many people immediately react by criticizing the NHS and then considering the private practice alternative. It is at this point that abuse can appear. Perhaps the consultant is not doing all that he might to ensure a speedy flow of out-patients through his department or, even worse, perhaps he is deliberately keeping patients waiting. Where is the evidence for either of these two criticisms? Out-patient clinic time is a precious commodity for the new referral, yet most out-patient clinics are taken up by patients re-attending the clinic. Whilst there are wide and unexplained differences in re-attendance rates this of course does not prove deliberate abuse on the part of the doctor. There are, however, other areas where anecdotal evidence points towards abuse. In some cases the number of clinics held per week is small and some consultants are infrequent attenders at their own clinics. Occasionally there are excellent reasons for non-attendance, but there are consultants who consistently delegate the running of the clinic to their juniors, rather than attend themselves.

Statistical evidence cannot be produced to show a direct link between bottlenecks in the NHS and the availability of private medicine. Although there is much criticism of the accuracy of NHS data, it is at least available. In the private sector we have no knowledge of the level of out-patient consultations and we can thus make no comment about its effect on waiting-lists or waiting time. The most telling evidence I can provide comes from a GP friend who has rewritten the *Tale of two cities*. In the one city is a general practice which advises its patients that referral for consultant opinion can result in a lengthy wait. Depending on which hospital and which consultant is selected this may mean 52 weeks to see an orthopaedic surgeon for severe hip pain or arthritic hands. Other conditions necessitating referral of adults to other surgeons will mean varying waits—increasing blindness because of cataracts 40 weeks, hearing difficulties 45 weeks, stomach ulcer 7 weeks, and pain and discomfort as a result of a prolapse 8 weeks. The referral of children for glue ears will mean a wait of 39 weeks, turn in an eye 12 weeks, and the examination of a heart murmur 12 weeks. In the case of emergencies there is virtually no waiting time for referral, but the waiting times quoted above can only be shortened in this large city if the general practitioner is prepared to make the time to 'shop around' and take the risk of referring patients to surgeons of whom the practitioner has little or no knowledge. In the other city the waiting times to see a consultant for most patients with similar conditions are considerably shorter and indeed in all cases the referral can be within one or two weeks.

The two practices are only three miles apart and they are, in fact, in the same city. The two practices share some of the same general practitioners. The difference in waiting time between the two practices is quite simply money. The majority of the patients in the second practice are in the following categories—insured with BUPA or its competitors, choose to pay cash to obtain a private out-patient consultation, middle class, eloquent, 'pushy', and prepared to enforce a shopping-around process, or even know how to 'beat the system'.

Exploiting waiting (for in-patient admission)

The wait for in-patient admission is the second major area of enormous tension. Time and time again patients are told that their operation will be next year in the NHS and next week in a private hospital. There are very many surgeons who have large and long

NHS waiting-lists, yet have very small and short private lists. How do they organize their work so well in one sector and so badly in the other? Does their conscience tolerate the different moral values? There are so many stories like the one which was reported in the *Bromsgrove and Droitwich Weekly Mail*,[2] outlining the problems for a hospital porter who was waiting for admission to the Midland Centre for Neurosurgery and Neurology. The patient was pictured lying in bed holding a letter from a consultant neurosurgeon. Under the headline, 'Patient tells of painful op dilemma', it explained that having spent nine months in pain, a further wait of many months could be expected unless he was prepared to pay up to £4000 for private treatment. The consultant stated that he would not normally point out that patients can have operations privately, except where people 'badger' him. He added, 'There is, of course, a beautifully-equipped hospital which is almost permanently half empty in Edgbaston, in which he could have his disc removed within the week if he had the funding.'

Whether in the private rooms or in the NHS out-patient clinic, the out-patient consultation provides a difficult ethical problem when there is a long in-patient waiting-list. As a further example, take the case of an elderly lady who had increasing trouble with vision in her right eye. Her general practitioner had referred her to an ophthalmologist. On discovering that she had a twelve week wait, she sought a private consultation and arrangements were made for her to see the consultant that day. He went on to explain that she needed an operation, but that it would be over two years before she would be seen in the NHS. The consultant then suggested she should have the operation done privately in two weeks' time, at a cost of £750. This was not a case of responding to the patient's enquiry by letting her know the alternatives. The consultant quite deliberately pushed the idea of private practice to the fore. I have heard numerous examples of this sort over the years, but to my knowledge there is no consistent evidence on the subject. Furthermore, when one starts to investigate such a situation, or even take it up on behalf of the patients, it is remarkable how frequently the patient, or their relatives, back off the issue. One is never quite sure whether this is because a patient has exaggerated the incident, or subsequently recognize that they might have misconstrued the conversation (which of course took place in a stressful situation). Alternatively they fear reprisal, in the sense that they think that the doctor, or other doctors, may withhold treatment and give priority to others. Until consumer organizations collect evidence on this subject on a systematic basis, there will be no way of knowing the extent of this type of unethical practice.

I did not tell the full story about the elderly lady who went to see the ophthalmologist. As she was unable to pay the £750 she decided to seek a second opinion. The second consultant's opinion was that she did not require an operation. To what extent does private practice lead to unnecessary operations? This is a subject much discussed in the United States and other countries where private medicine is much more dominant within the health care system. I would not suggest that it is a serious problem in Britain, but it does occur.

Unfulfilled contracts

There are two difficulties in looking at the subject of unfulfilled contracts. Firstly, what should one expect during a working week and how much contractual time should be allowed for on-call, emergencies, attending meetings, and administrative work? While some surgeons operate three or four times a week and do two or three out-patient sessions, there are those who content themselves with two operating sessions per week, two out-patient clinics and a couple of one-hour ward rounds. The rest of the time is allocated to on-call and emergency work (which is mainly undertaken by the junior staff), committee work, and administration. Secondly, given that we accept that a notional half-day is approximately three and a half hours, do consultants give value for money during one such session in an out-patient clinic or an operating-theatre? Clearly one expects some variability in the way people work. Many surgeons are very enthusiastic and their operating sessions go on for much more than three and a half hours, often to the annoyance of the nurses and other staff who have to work past their normal hours in order to complete the operating list. Even for those surgeons who do not work over the three and a half hour period, there are very good reasons why lists might not always last the full half-day. Some theatre schedules are so tight that they have difficulty in coping with emergencies. It is not always easy to predict with accuracy how long an operation will take and some surgeons operate more quickly than others. Factors such as these lead to some sessions being longer than others and to some surgeons undertaking more work in a year than others. There are, however, those who do not fully utilize their lists. I am prepared to dismiss as exaggerated the claim by a junior doctor that for a whole year his consultant operated on only one private case in each list and then left the remainder of the (NHS) work-load to his registrar, but I am aware that there are consultants who personally do few of the operations on some of their lists. I can give an example of an orthopaedic team (that is the consultant with his senior registrar or registrar and other junior staff) which operates on 600–700 cases per annum, but the consultant himself will operate on only between 100–150 patients. If the consultant was supervising his junior staff and teaching them operating techniques, or alternatively working elsewhere in the NHS, then one might not be concerned. Unfortunately, this is not always the case. A newly appointed senior registrar was told by his consultant to turn up at the theatre at 10.00 a.m. The senior registrar assumed that he (the senior registrar) was not to start an operating list on his own until the consultant surgeon had seen his work. Presumably the consultant was to start the first case on the list and then meet the senior registrar. The senior registrar arrived at the theatre in time to gown up for 10 o'clock, only to find no patients and no surgeon. Shortly before 10.00 a.m. a message came through from the anaesthetist, who rushed in explaining that he and the surgeon had been held up at the private hospital and would the senior registrar start the NHS list.

Leaving the NHS operating list to junior staff is not an infrequent occurrence and there are scheduled lists for which the consultant is never seen, year in and year out, because he is actually operating elsewhere. Unsupervised junior staff are sometimes forced to tackle difficult operations for which they have inadequate training. Evidence regarding this type of abuse is very often anecdotal in the NHS, but there is no need for it to be so. It is quite simple to go to sources and identify how many operations of each type each team and surgeon do per annum and compare with those elsewhere in the region and the country. It is only recently that the Association of Surgeons and of Anaesthetists of Great Britain and Ireland[3] have begun to study deaths in hospital following surgery and this may produce more evidence on this subject.

Mrs G goes private?

There is no conclusive evidence which proves that NHS staff can be blamed for long waiting-lists. There is a strong association between industrial action and the growth in waiting-lists, but the case regarding the abuse of the NHS through private medicine has to be considered as 'not proven'. There is clearly some abuse, but the absence of any mechanism to study the work of individual surgeons in the private sector means that the discussion remains at the level of gossip. If I were Mrs G I would have a jaundiced view about private care. I would fear that private hospitals, the financial organizations that support them, and the surgeons who work in those hospitals know that unless there are substantial NHS waiting-lists their income would be much lower. We trust the medical profession not to abuse the position which in the commercial world would never be allowed. The system itself is unfair. It pretends to be one which allows and encourages competition, but it is not a proper competitive market. In the commercial world in which Mrs G and her husband have worked, it is not normal practice for people to work for two competing organizations. Perhaps she should refer the matter to the Office of Fair Trading. The system appears unfair and she would like to ensure not only that justice is being done, but that justice is being seen to be done. If there is nothing to hide, there is presumably no reason why she should not be allowed a full presentation of the facts about the work-load in private hospitals and the way in which work is conducted within NHS hospitals. She wants to know which surgeons:

(a) work hard to eliminate or minimize waiting time and succeed;
(b) work genuinely hard to eliminate waiting time and fail through lack of resources;
(c) do the minimum required and are quite pleased to see a long waiting-list;
(d) actually exploit the situation for their own gain.

If none fall into the latter two groups, then Mrs G and British society will have the most enormous confidence boost for its health service and medical profession and also the hard evidence to support the demand for an increase of revenue to health care services. If, however, a substantial proportion fall into the latter two groups then she would begin to understand why the health care system has a bit of work to do before it can justify additional resources.

Why does Mrs G not go privately? When she went on to the waiting-list her husband was a foreman in a local factory and she had a small part-time job, but they were saving for his imminent retirement. She could sink all her savings into paying for the operation, but is reluctant to do so and, to my surprise and admiration, feels that she should not jump the queue ahead of others who might need an operation. Her naïve faith in the NHS is remarkable. So during the five years that she has waited in increasing pain, her surgeon has done hundreds of private operations and earned thousands of pounds on top of his NHS salary. Mrs G is just part of the queue that richer people jump.

References

1. Lewis, E. B. (1981). Private practice. *British Medical Journal*, **282**, 841–2.
2. Lennox, T. (1983). Patient tells of painful op dilemma. *Bromsgrove Weekly Mail* 11 November, 6.
3. Devlin, H. B., and Lunn, J. N. (1986). Confidential inquiry into perioperative deaths. *British Medical Journal*, **292**, 1622–3.

7

What's it like so far?

Summarizing the evidence

Signs of spring are beginning to appear. The privet hedge is starting to grow and I need to collect my thoughts before venturing into the garden. Having looked at five explanations I have found that each one has been inadequate.

1. The claim that waiting-lists are inaccurate is justified to the extent that it is technically true, but there is no justification for using such an argument for failing to act on behalf of the thousands who are waiting far too long in pain and suffering. We cannot afford to swell the ranks of those academics, epidemiologists, clinicians, managers, and politicians who spend their time arguing about the details and concepts of measurement. This first explanation must not be offered to my neighbour—it is merely an excuse for inactivity.

2. The iceberg explanation is very powerful. On a national scale the evidence supports the contention that the more we do, the more we find that needs to be done. We might console ourselves with the fact that achievements in health care are constantly pushing back the barriers of knowledge and over the years we gradually treat and cure more illnesses at an earlier stage than before. Health care improves, but people have to wait at the edge of progress. On a forty-year time-scale the explanation is fine, but there are two major reservations. Waiting-lists do not consist of patients whose illnesses are at the frontiers of medical science. In the main they are awaiting treatment for commonplace and sometimes relatively minor operations. They are those who

63

are left behind whilst the NHS treats the urgent or exciting cases. The second reservation is that waiting time for such operations varies from locality to locality and we do not know why. If some districts avoid waiting-lists for hernias, is it because they handle all the demand, or simply that they fail even to put such cases on the waiting-list? The iceberg theory is a national explanation, but it has less validity at a local level. It is an explanation I can offer to an audience of three quarters of a million, but not so helpful when I meet my neighbour.

3. To argue that the NHS is short of money seems a fairly safe strategy. The evidence available shows that Britain spends less on health care than many other comparable countries. All the professional groups in the NHS say that it requires more money and they can all produce eloquent support for their case. The weakness with this argument is that there is not necessarily a straightforward association between the provision of funds and the length of a waiting-list. Simply proving that the NHS needs more money does not prove that more is needed to shorten waiting-lists. There is no proof so far that all those districts which have long lists are short of cash and all those which have short lists are well off. For some it is true and for others not. It is easy to claim that there is a shortage of resources, but we cannot automatically assume that explains every long waiting-list. I can only use the shortage of resources argument with my neighbour if that is true of her district.

4. Explaining waiting-lists by claims of inefficiency is not satisfactory. Yet again the evidence shows that whilst inefficient use of resources is a fact of life and must make an overall contribution to long lists, it does not, as an explanation, stand up to a district by district analysis. Long waiting-lists occur in efficient and inefficient districts and this is another explanation that can only be offered to my neighbour if it is true of her district.

5. Finally, I could move into the treacherous waters of industrial relations and private practice. Here again there is the

unsatisfactory dichotomy between factors which on a national level have an influence on waiting-lists, yet at a local level their impact is highly variable. Overall, the level of evidence about the impact of private medicine on the length of waiting-lists is poor in the sense that it is anecdotal and lacking in hard facts. All too often it is an explanation that generates too much heat and too little light. It is a sinister explanation that worries the poor and does not seem to concern the rich. For my neighbour to prove it has affected her wait, she needs access to information to which she has no legal right and the time and resources to act as a private detective. In the absence of evidence, I cannot offer this explanation to my neighbour.

My winter's studies have taught me that no one explanation can be used to account for Britain's hospital waiting-lists. If I were a statistician perhaps I could juggle all the facts at my disposal and estimate how much impact each of these explanations has and whether the five together explained the existence of the waiting-lists—I doubt it. Even if such an equation explained the British waiting-lists, it could not adequately account for the enormous variation in the size of lists and the length of wait that occurs from town to town in this country. There appears to be no national explanation and thus no national solution. I am left with the need to study each list individually.

Where does this leave Mrs G?

If I am unable to provide my neighbour with an answer that solves the nation's problems (i.e. one that can be used over every hedge and fence in Britain), then perhaps I should review the facts as they affect the particular list on which she waits. The facts are as follows:

1. At the end of 1981 Mrs G was referred to an orthopaedic surgeon.

2. In March 1982 she saw the surgeon and was placed on an in-patient waiting-list.

3. The list remained unreviewed for over three years.

4. When the review ultimately took place it left her feeling even more uncertain and gave no promise of any date of admission.

5. The list has over 2000 patients and is far larger than is needed to schedule patients.

6. The hospital deals with some specialist referrals which might take priority over her case.

7. The district she lives in has a very low proportion of elderly people.

8. The waiting-list is in a district which is not short of resources. It has more trauma and orthopaedic beds than virtually any other district in Britain and is very well supplied for medical staff.

9. Many of the beds lie unused because theatre provision is inadequate in the hospital where she awaits admission. This fact has been clear to the regional authority for at least ten years.

10. The district health authority has under-used theatres in neighbouring hospitals and also has a temporary theatre tent lying unused in the grounds of the hospital in which Mrs G hopes to be a patient.

11. An external report by management consultants recommended various courses of action to improve the situation, but few have been implemented.

12. Strikes by NHS staff in the past ten years have led to a reduction in the number of cases admitted to her hospital.

13. During the time she has been on the list her surgeon has earned (legitimately) thousands and thousands of pounds from private practice.

Perhaps I ought to move house or not cut my hedge! For five years I have avoided studying the detail of her case, on the grounds that any attempted intervention on my part might simply lead to Mrs G being promoted over the head of another equally deserving patient. I had a naïve faith in the system I worked in. Now that has been shattered I have to move from trying to explain the situation to trying to change it. This book now concludes by looking at what has been tried and what should be tried.

8

What has been tried?

Long and lengthening waiting-lists have not gone unchallenged. Various attempts have been made to improve the situation at national and local levels, varying from sustained effort to short-lived frenzy. It is clear that the various efforts have not eliminated or reduced waiting-lists, but they have made some contribution in publicizing the problem and resisting an even worse deterioration. There have been occasional successes, although it has to be said that these have been in particular specialties, in particular localities, and very often for only a short period. I have grouped these initiatives into three categories—the individual initiatives of a patient, relative, consultant, journalist, or MP; the collective efforts of clinicians, managers, and others within a health district; and finally, efforts on a national scale.

Individual initiatives

All types of people try to put right the injustices with which they are faced. These are just a few of the methods employed.

Special pleading

Patients, relatives, and general practitioners occasionally break through the waiting barrier by eloquent special pleading. The well-argued case, explaining why a particular patient should have a higher priority than others and avoid a long wait, can lead to early admission. One suspects that this manoeuvre is most frequently tried by the educated middle class, but there is no real evidence. Special pleading can reduce waiting, but only for one patient at a time and always at the expense of another. It offers no contribution to the overall problem.

Making a nuisance of yourself

An alternative form of queue-jumping can be achieved by making life uncomfortable for hospital staff. Constant pressure in the form of letters and telephone calls can wear down the consultant, his secretary, and the hospital staff so that they give in and admit the patient at the centre of the furore in order to get some peace. Similar tactics can be applied by writing letters of complaint to the community health council, district health authority, and members of Parliament. Such tactics cause resentment, but they can alter priority. This method seldom achieves more than reducing the waiting time for one individual patient at the expense of another.

Raising a stink

Exposing the plight of the sick is newsworthy to the media, providing that it is not too repetitive. Typical of this method was the *Guardian*'s report by Polly Toynbee,[1] raising the plight of an individual with the hope of achieving an improvement for all patients. Unfortunately, even well-written pieces in papers such as the *Guardian* rarely have much impact. This vivid description of the pain and suffering of patients awaiting treatment at the London Hospital was published in 1983. A year later the waiting-list showed little change. This method can put public pressure on the hospital and its staff, but again is mainly a way of changing priorities between patients. In my experience it seldom stimulates significant change for all the patients on a list.

It is not just patients, relatives, and the press who get heated about waiting-lists. Hospital staff also express concern. Sometimes this boils over into public criticism of the NHS. Consultants commonly point out the dangers of a lack of resources and appear under banner headlines like, 'Patients will die on the list'. This pressure sometimes takes extreme forms, to the extent where some are prepared to sabotage internal relationships and lay all, or most, of the cards on the table for all to see. One example of this is the tactics employed by an orthopaedic surgeon, who having made several attempts to obtain additional resources by normal methods, decided on shock tactics. He held an open meeting in the town hall for all patients on his waiting-list and invited the television cameras to be present. Headlines were created, including the statement that one 85-year-old lady would have to wait 40 years for an operation. Suddenly the apparently ponderous bureaucracy of health authorities was stirred into response. After acrimonious debate additional resources were provided. Unfortunately, the size and length of the waiting-list did not reduce dramatically, but on this occasion the ploy did result in the provision of additional resources.

This is, however, a tactic that a group of people can only use once. If it does not work there are no cards left to play. It virtually always creates antagonism. In the case cited above, because of the tactics used by the surgeon, the transfer of resources to the district concerned was nearly vetoed. Such tactics also produce very strong counter-attacks, and any surgeon trying such a method is almost assured that every element of his case and his practice, right down to the speed at which he operates, will come under scrutiny. As a manoeuvre it needs a very strong case, with few or no flaws, and also the knowledge that there is a very good chance of obtaining the resources required.

Put it on computer!

One of the more impressive individual initiatives has been the sustained effort of Mr John Heddle, MP. Having discovered that there were significant variations in the length of time patients waited in various parts of the country, he became party to the idea of arranging for patients to travel from areas where there is a long wait, to places where there is a much shorter waiting time—a sort of 'busing' of patients. Having succeeded in transferring one of his constituents from Birmingham to Aberdeen for an operation, he suggested that a national computer bank be established which would register all patients in the country waiting for surgery and enable patients to be matched with surgeons who were willing and able to operate earlier than those in the patient's locality.[2] The idea of this system was that it would provide a national data-base to which general practitioners could refer.

Not surprisingly, as with many novel ideas, there are some problems. There is some reservation about confidentiality of records, not all doctors and patients will want to participate in such a system and it would have to be a very large data-base to keep up-to-date with the changing circumstances of patients and their conditions. Although this mechanism might help re-allocate patients, it does not overcome the fundamental fact that at the current rate of work there are far too few districts and surgeons able to offer enough spare capacity to meet the demand. Mr Heddle's idea is currently being tried out in one of the fourteen English regions.

Local initiatives

Clinicians, managers, and health authority members frequently try to tackle waiting-list problems. Their efforts are not so often publicized, either in the local press or in professional journals. This may be partly because efforts have failed, but also perhaps because success in this area is not a subject which excites the media. Furthermore, there is no tradition of writing up managerial work of this type in medical, or even in management journals. Let us look at a number of initiatives which have been made in various health authorities.

Contracting work out

Some health authorities have attempted to reduce waiting-lists by arranging a contract with another hospital or health authority to undertake the work. This is a localized version of the idea proposed by John Heddle. Although there have been a rash of such contracts recently, the idea is not exactly new. Ever since the establishment of the NHS in 1948, regional health authorities (formerly regional hospital boards) have frequently contracted with non-NHS hospitals to treat and care for NHS patients with an agreed financial arrangement. What is new is the idea of this arrangement being undertaken specifically with the intent of reducing waiting-lists. One example of this procedure occurred in 1984 when Bath Health District paid for elderly patients to have hip operations at the King Edward VII Hospital in Midhurst, Sussex and in the following year the same authority paid the private Bath Clinic to undertake over 120 ENT children's operations. In the latter case the operations were actually performed on Sunday afternoons by surgeons who worked in the Bath Health District.

A different form of contracting work is between NHS health authorities. A contract is struck between a health authority with a large waiting-list problem and another that has some spare capacity. An example of this type of contract was the deal between South-East Kent District Health Authority and the Guy's and New Cross Hospitals in the Lewisham and North Southwark Health Authority in 1983 and 1984. South-East Kent had a large waiting-list in orthopaedic surgery for some years and wished to reduce the backlog of patients waiting for hip replacement. The authority agreed a contract with the Guy's and New Cross orthopaedic unit to undertake 100 hip replacement operations in return for a lump sum of £100 000. The agreement stipulated that if any complications arose from surgery the patients concerned would be treated at New Cross Hospital until well enough to be discharged. Complications not arising directly from surgery would, if possible, be treated in South-East Kent. At a very early stage in the contract the need to review patients in the out-patient department was confirmed. Many patients had been on the in-patient waiting-list for a considerable period, some patients were no longer fit for surgery, having developed other medical problems, and some no longer wished to have the operation. The contract was completed successfully, but certain observations and reservations were made. Pre-operative assessment is absolutely essential, especially where long and unreviewed lists are concerned. Even when lists are updated regularly, pre-operative review is highly desirable, otherwise the situation arises where one surgeon assesses a patient and another surgeon sees the patient for the first time on admission. Clearly this gives little time for assessment. Even if there is no delay between the patient being seen by each of the surgeons, there might be a difference of opinion about diagnosis and the treatment selected. Pre-operative assessment by the surgeon and team doing the operation is fundamental to British medical practice.

One of the ironies of health authorities striking bargains with one another is that so often it is the 'poor' authority which is paying the 'better off' authority to do the work. The effect of this short term expedient seems to be a benefit for all, but it does run the risk of slowing down the process of redistribution of revenue.

Contracts between NHS authorities, and between the NHS and the private sector appear to be quite successful in particular localities. They can help to reduce waiting-lists, but unless they increase in frequency and scale are unlikely to fundamentally alter the waiting-list position on a national scale. They are in any case usually a short term expedient prior to a proper redistribution of resources between specialties and districts.

Intensive study

Occasionally clinicians, managers, and health authority members make a cohesive and sustained effort to reduce waiting-lists. The method of tackling the problem is to set up some form of working party, sometimes with outside management consultants or clinical help, making a detailed study of the problems faced by the service concerned. Such studies gather extensive data about the services in the hospital or district and seek the opinion of people within the district about solutions to the problems. Data may be collected about bed use, theatre allocation and use, staffing levels, and equipment needs. Waiting-lists are sometimes reviewed along lines discussed earlier. The effect of concentrating thought into one area can have many benefits. Solutions are discovered for some of the deficiencies and attitudes can be loosened, thus allowing changes in allocation or provision of resources or a rethink of working practice that enables some improvements to be made. The results of such studies can lead to an increase in throughput, a reduction in waiting-lists or even both. Sometimes they achieve little or no progress and occasionally make matters worse by raising expectations that are not met, leaving the organization in even deeper despondency.

No one knows the level of success of this method, as the reviews are seldom published, particularly when they fail. My experience of some twenty or more such studies is that they generally achieve some level of success, although they can quickly revert to previous unsatisfactory levels unless clinicians, management, and the health authority are committed to constant review. I have also observed that the performance failures are virtually always associated with poorly run divisions in which clinicians seldom meet, do not consider data, and are not supported by management.

Other local initiatives

Local initiatives are constantly being attempted by surgeons, managers, and others to ease waiting-time problems. Some of these include:

● Running operating-theatres in evenings and at weekends in order to increase throughput. Whilst this requires some additional revenue, there are many occasions where staff have worked voluntarily for a number of months in order to reduce waiting-lists.

● One health authority undertook a three week 'blitz', in which ENT surgeons were loaned resources (theatres and beds) by other colleagues and then operated for 12 sessions per week for three weeks.

● Making hospital facilities available directly to general practitioners (e.g. for X-rays, pathology tests, orthopaedic collars, etc.), who can prescribe the service required, thus avoiding the need to refer the patient to a hospital consultant. The level of 'open access', as this practice is called, varies from district to district and GPs not provided with such a service feel they can contribute to a reduction in out-patient waiting time if such facilities are provided.

● Bringing forward appointments or purchases of equipment to an earlier date in order to make a speedier start on a waiting-list. This occurs, for example, when a new hospital (or phase of hospital) is scheduled to open, but funding is released for appointments to be made ahead of the opening date.

● Expansion of the use of day-case surgery, which reduces the amount of time spent on traditional wards. The use of day case techniques for certain conditions varies widely from surgeon to surgeon and district to district. Sometimes the reasons for failing to take up such techniques are the lack of facilities, equipment, or training. If these matters are corrected, then the resulting increase in day case activity can contribute to waiting-list and waiting time reduction.

National initiatives

Apart from expressions of concern, little has been done at a national level explicitly to combat waiting-lists. Three initiatives are worthy of note.

Working party on orthopaedic
in-patient and out-patient waiting time

In thirty years the NHS has had only one national working party on waiting-lists. The choice of orthopaedics was quite simply made because orthopaedics not only had one of the largest problems, but a growing problem, particularly in respect of the long-wait patients. Under the chairmanship of Mr Robert Duthie, a leading orthopaedic surgeon, the working party was established in 1979.[3] Its membership was selected by a Labour Government and before the Working Party had met, a general election brought in a Conservative Government. The membership was vetted by the incoming government and remained unchanged. We must have been a very apolitical lot! When the Duthie Working Party was set up a number of its members were somewhat sceptical of the attitude of the Government and the Department of Health about the value of working parties. There seemed to be an attitude that if you select fifteen good men and true, get them to talk about the subject, and reproduce their combined thoughts, such wisdom could then be disseminated throughout the service and produce some effective change. Two types of scepticism were present. Firstly, some of us did not feel that we, or anyone else, were knowledgable enough about the subject and that a preferred method of working would be to actually find out more about the problem at hand. It was interesting to see that any attempt that bordered on research and data-gathering was not encouraged by the civil servants, and that much of the data collection and analysis undertaken by the working party was done by the members themselves and NHS personnel. The second reservation related to the notion of publishing a report and expecting that if it was good enough its dissemination would produce some change. One suspects that in some quarters the whole thing was considered merely as a political ploy to keep the heat off criticisms which had been levelled consistently at the governments of both political parties. Whilst a working party is sitting, one can deflect questions, on the grounds that the subject is under discussion, and once the report has been published, one can then refer critics to the collective ramblings of the individuals concerned. Many of us had very serious reservations about this as a method for actually addressing the problem in hand, namely reducing time and waiting numbers of orthopaedic patients in England.

Given this scepticism, what has been the contribution of the Duthie Working Party Report? Its terms of reference were 'to recommend measures designed to eliminate excessive waiting-time for out-patient appointments and in-patient treatment' in the orthopaedic specialty. The Working Party Report showed that variations in size of waiting-lists and waiting time were not simply due to shortage of resources and that there were the most enormous variations between districts with regard to waiting experience, input of resources and use of resources. It suggested that districts should undertake internal reviews in the hope that as a consequence there would be improvements in throughput and a reduction in waiting-lists and time. The reaction of districts was, however, spasmodic and there is little evidence that such activity has significantly increased or been conducted more successfully than prior to the Duthie Report.

How effective was the working party? Its report may have been politically useful in keeping the lid on the clamour, but the situation deteriorated. In defence, it might be said that the implementation of the 'Duthie report' proposals and the adoption of good practice throughout the country has probably saved the situation from being even worse. One could be cynical and say that the time spent by surgeons reading the report and attending meetings to discuss it has actually reduced the amount of operating time available and made matters worse. In 1978, before the working party was established, there were 112 999 patients on the in-patient waiting-list and 32 per cent of the non-urgent patients waited over one year for admission. There were enormous variations between English districts regarding waiting time. Some districts had hardly any waiting-list, but at the other extreme there were a couple of districts where 70 per cent of the patients waited over a year for treatment. Five years later in 1983, after the Duthie report had been written, published, and discussed, the position was that the total list had risen to 142 113, 40 per cent of non-urgent patients waited over a year for admission and there was an even larger variation in waiting time between districts.

College of Health

Despite the increase in consumer-association activity in the past ten years, the NHS has not been faced with much systematic analytical criticism from community health councils and organizations like the Patients' Association. In the main, criticisms have been either anecdotal, concerned with individual patient complaints, or related to national policies.

All are vital but all can easily be dodged by the NHS. Recently the College of Health has started to produce comparative tables about in-patient waiting time. Obviously it is constrained by the limitation of the national data collected, but it has broken new ground by naming districts with long waiting times and encouraging its readership to 'shop around'.[4] Its modest start probably marks a new era in consumer interest and it has taken the major step of breaking through the confidentiality barrier. For far too long comparative information about health care services has not been available to the consumer. The population is entitled to know the weakness and strength of its own service and what causes the problems.

Having made an admirable start, it has yet to change the waiting experience for many people. Maybe it is too soon for that. The College of Health does however have a problem—so far it only reaches a small percentage of the population.

A waiting-list fund

In 1986 the Secretary of State for Wales established a special waiting-list fund for Welsh health authorities and an additional million pounds was made available during the 1986/7 financial year. Later in the same year the Secretary of State for Health and Social Security announced a similar initiative in England, scheduled to commence in April 1987. It is to last for two years and £25 000 000 was set aside for each of the years. These are the first national initiatives which have been supported by specific financing. Critics have argued that it is too little, too late, and simply a vote-catching exercise, but health authority staff, who have long claimed additional resources are needed, have now been provided with a challenge. Clearly, far too many have been caught 'with their trousers down' and one Welsh authority has already handed back over £200 000 which it could not use in the time-scale offered. Admittedly the Welsh initiative demanded a speedy response, but the people of the valleys must be disappointed with the inflexibility demonstrated by their health authority.

Final comment on this attempt must be left until March 1988. It will be classed as successful only if the number of patients treated in the NHS has continued to increase and the number of patients waiting over a year (currently 132 000) has been at least halved.

And Mrs G?

Perhaps all this effort has prevented further deterioration, but for the individual patient like Mrs G our efforts have failed. In her case no one has specially pleaded her cause, nor raised a stink, and neither has her case been picked up by the media. Her district's efforts to review the problem have not yet yielded a solution. She has never heard of The College of Health, and the Duthie Working Party did nothing for her, despite the fact that she lived next door to a member of the only national working party on waiting-lists!

References

1. Toynbee, P. (1983). A painful experience. *Guardian* 12 December, 10.
2. Heddle, J. (1982). *No waiting: a solution to reducing hospital waiting lists*. Conservative Political Centre, London.
3. Duthie, R. B. (Chairman) (1981). *Orthopaedic services: waiting time for out-patient appointments and in-patient treatment: report of a working party*. DHSS, HMSO, London.
4. College of Health (1985). *Guide to hospital waiting lists 1985*. The College of Health and Inter-Authority Comparisons and Consultancy.

9

What should be tried?

The previous chapter outlined some of the things which have been tried over the past forty years. I do not suggest that these efforts should stop, but in view of their ineffectiveness, they need to be supplemented by new initiatives. I propose a seven-pronged attack. The first three ideas can and should be implemented within one year and the others should be discussed in that same period and implemented within five years.

1. Publically investigate the blackspots and publish the results.
2. Make available existing information to the public.
3. Collect and publish information about out-patient waiting time.
4. Compensate patients for long waits.
5. Encourage the study of 'good practice'.
6. Clarify the consultants' contract.
7. Set up a health inspectorate.

Things to do now

1. Investigate the blackspots and publish the results

An independent investigation should be established to examine those districts where a significantly high proportion of patients have been consistently subjected to long periods of waiting. The purpose of the investigations should be to establish the precise reasons for the waiting in each of the districts selected. Currently the only readily available comparative data on waiting time is from form SBH203. In 1985, the College of Health published a list of authorities which had over 40 per cent of patients waiting over a year for admission.[1] Using more recent information, a study should be made in those districts which consistently keep a large proportion of patients waiting over a year.

The investigators should be given access to detailed local data about the allocation and use of beds, day-case facilities, operating-theatres and out-patient departments, and should study the total workload of all staff. Opinions about the service offered should be sought from management, clinical and nursing staff, the district health authority, community health council, more general consumer opinion, and the regional health authority. The results of the investigation should be published.

2. Make available existing information to the public

Patients are entitled to be fully informed about the way their local health services are being managed. To achieve this there must be the capacity to compare local performance with that in other parts of the country, as is done in local government. More comparative data was published in the time of Lord Shaftesbury than today. We have replaced clerks by computers, but get less information. Waiting-list and waiting time information for every district, hospital, and surgeon could easily be made available on Teletext, Oracle, or Prestel. Such data would only provide the basic knowledge about waiting, but the public (especially consumer representatives like community health councils, the College of Health, and the press) should also have access to comparative data about the level of resources in order to find out what is done with those resources and the results of that activity. Some parts of the health service will howl with anguish about the dangers of publishing inaccurate data but they have a simple remedy in their hands—produce accurate data!

It is not that the information is secret—it is available and can be collected, providing an individual patient or newspaper reporter has the tenacity to go round two hundred health districts. As the health service itself has this information readily available, there should be no reason why it cannot be made available to their customers.

It will be argued that such data is insensitive to the complexities of life, but the fact that, for instance, a group of doctors in one district is seeing fewer patients than elsewhere in the country should not be hidden from the patients in that locality. It should form the basis of a dialogue between the clinicians and the locality as to why this is so. It may be that it is a deliberate policy in order to expand the treatment of a particular disease, but the district itself should be party to the decision. As resources are finite there is no harm in an individual locality deciding whether it wishes to see the expansion of a particular treatment of a rare disease for the benefit of the region or the nation *vis-à-vis* the decreased number of other operations for its own locality.

It is also important that comparative data is used by health authority members, managers, and health care professionals such as doctors and nurses. One would expect the enormous variations in performance to be the subject of comment and debate in professional journals.

Finally, the opening up of access to data should not be restricted to the NHS. The public, the planners, and the managers of the NHS will need to know what work is being done in private hospitals. The establishment of a system similar to the NHS Hospital Activity Analysis, which is made available to regional health authorities, seems an absolute minimum requirement. The public too should be able to compare the use made of private and NHS hospitals.

3. Collect and publish information about out-patient waiting time

National collection of information about waiting time for an out-patient appointment is long overdue. It is needed for two purposes. Firstly a national study will enable us to identify which districts and specialties have the worst problems. This will help us focus our attention on the locations that need our help. Secondly, that same information could be made available to patients, general practitioners, community health councils, and the public in each locality in order to enable a certain amount of 'shopping around' to be done. For this second purpose it would not be necessary to publish all the national information, but select from it the information on a zonal basis for each district and its surrounding districts.

This type of information-gathering has proved difficult in the past, as there have been arguments over what definitions should be used. I would suggest the enormous variations in waiting time make some of the arguments seem rather pedantic. The information required of each district is:

(1) the number of weeks wait until the next non-urgent appointment for each surgeon;

(2) for those surgeons holding separate specialist clinics (e.g. varicose vein, laser, foot clinics) the waiting time for that clinic should also be recorded.

This information should be collected on a three-monthly basis. Providing each authority supplied the data, an information service to give this information to health authorities, family practitioner committees, and community health councils could be established by the use of one microcomputer and just two staff.

Things to discuss now

4. Compensate patients for long waits

Should patients who have waited over a year for treatment receive compensation? I do not pretend to have fully researched this idea, but there may be merit in changing the incentives and disincentives that currently exist. Such payment could be made from the district health authority's budget with no reimbursement from regional or DHSS funds. As an additional incentive to districts to put their own house in order, their senior staff could attract financial penalties for having long waiting-lists. Managers would not receive full payment for the general manager's duties and merit award

payments to surgeons and anaesthetists in the district concerned
should be temporarily suspended.

5. Encourage the study of 'good practice'

The Medical Research Council is a body which tries to ensure
the rigorous testing of new forms of treatment. There is no
equivalent organization which applies similar rigour to the
application of known techniques and the management of services.
It would be worth considering establishing an organization which
undertook three roles.

(a) The study of the way in which clinicians adopt new forms of treatment

Much treatment has already been subjected to vigorous
randomized controlled trials and has been found to be satisfactory,
but the uptake of these ideas is haphazard. Subjects suitable for
study would include the use of day-case surgery for operations
such as varicose veins, meniscectomy and haemorrhoids. Another
subject is the uptake of medicines like cimetidine, which are
claimed to reduce the need for admission for some patients and
the length of stay in hospital of others.

(b) The study of the economic impact of clinical practice

Key decisions about whether patients should be admitted, and if
so, how long they should stay in hospital, are taken firstly on
clinical grounds. However, the influence of social conditions,
availability of hospital resources, and the level of primary care
support services are enormously influential in these same decisions.
The majority of health care expenditure is on hospital services
and yet we cannot adequately explain why patients awaiting the
same operation are kept in hospital for such different periods of
time. Length of stay patterns and admission rates vary enormously
and their variation is much wider than can be explained by
differences in case mix or the incidence of disease. There is no
organization in this country which can find the time to study this
subject systematically.

(c) The study of management in medicine

Managers and clinicians often talk about good practice. For instance, I have repeatedly heard people say how useful it is or would be if all GPs in a district were circulated with information about in-patient and out-patient waiting-lists. It is claimed that this enables GPs to make an informed choice about where, and to whom, to refer their patients. I know of no published evidence which has shown that this practice has altered referral patterns and whether such change was for the better. So many of our 'good practices' are just conventions or statements of the apparently obvious. Such ideas should be subjected to properly controlled trials to ascertain what impact they really have. Those which are beneficial should be more widely promulgated and those which show no results should be labelled clearly as 'fashion'. Subjects might include—the use of social workers on ward rounds to aid earlier discharge, the computerization of waiting-lists, contracting surgery to neighbouring districts or private hospitals, the appointment of managers in surgical departments, and so on.

We need to pay much more attention to implementing successful clinical research and promoting research into the way medicine is managed.

6. Clarify the consultants' contract

For years any suggestion that the work load of consultants should be monitored has been frowned upon. The professional is hurt when anyone suggests that he cannot be trusted to do an honest day's work for a day's pay. The response is an indignant suggestion that any such study will only reveal that more pay will have to be made for the excessive hours worked. I can understand that the top class professional dislikes the innuendo, but on reflection he must realize that there are two reasons why such monitoring must be done. Firstly, justice must not only be done, but it must be seen to be done. The profession has no means of showing the consumer what its members do and if they are not prepared to establish such a mechanism they will always be open to suspicion. This is particularly the case when the profession operates a confidential merit award system and its surgeons are in a position where their failure to cope with an NHS work-load can be financially advantageous. Secondly, some of the profession manifestly do not do a fair day's work for a fair day's pay. Court cases have clearly illustrated the types of financial abuse which are possible and there is some evidence that a substantial minority of surgeons have a very small operative work-load. The medical profession should not get annoyed with its critics for suggesting that reform is needed. The profession itself should have taken the lead and some of its members admit this.[2] The time has come to look carefully at the consultant contract. Among the issues to be considered are the following:

(a) An examination of each surgeon's work-load: each authority (district and region) should be quite clear about how much time and how much activity should reasonably be expected.

(b) If private work is to continue to be allowed, should not the surgeon declare his private work-load? Most other employers are very concerned about work done, even when it is outside the formal working hours. Gas board officials do not routinely fit gas pipes in private homes with the blessing of the Gas Board. The medical profession is the only one that is allowed to 'moonlight' at the expense of the employer.

(c) Should private work be completely separated from the NHS? This option might risk a wholesale move of surgeons to the private sector, but if a large enough proportion were prepared to stay in the NHS, they could be given increased remuneration to compensate for the loss of private income.

(d) Should merit awards be openly linked to service achievement? How many of the existing holders have been given an award for services to the NHS (i.e. not for research or teaching) and what is their actual work-load? Should the merit award be permanent, or for a fixed term and then re-assessed?

Any such discussions will be incredibly emotional and must be handled tactfully (unlike my suggestions!). This is an enormous threat to some people's income, livelihood, and life-style. None of us welcome such a challenge.

7. Set up a health inspectorate

In the field of mental illness and mental handicap a number of enquiries into the abuse of patients led to the establishment of a form of independent inspectorate. The Health Advisory Service and the National Development Team for the Mentally Handicapped are now responsible for visiting mental illness, geriatric, and mental handicap hospitals and services. No comparable organization exists to provide a systematic external assessment of acute services. Hospitals do receive visits from the Health and Safety Inspectorate, fire officers, and professional bodies responsible for the training of doctors and nurses, but their efforts are unco-ordinated and incomplete. Waiting time is just one of a number of issues which could be addressed by an inspectorate or agency which had the power to visit and the role of disseminating good practice. An independent assessment of standards of service would provide an additional incentive for managers and clinicians to achieve higher standards. Currently the NHS has a large number of virtually toothless visiting agencies and the patient only has recourse to a complaints procedure which culminates in the Ombudsman or the courts. Neither the inspectors nor the complaints system make any use of the masses of NHS data which could provide a firm foundation for scanning the performance of health authorities and spotlighting possible poor performance. The reconsideration of an inspectorate for the NHS is long overdue.

Will these proposals eliminate waiting time?

These seven ideas are not original and some readers may think it strange that an author should have the naïvity or arrogance to put together such a package. What chance is there of success if these seven proposals are seriously acted upon? Let us look at this through the eyes of three caricatures, the pessimist, the optimist, and the realist. The pessimist would argue that you can never get rid of waiting-lists. The two principal reasons in support of this view are firstly that the ability to develop new techniques and treatment will never ever be matched by an ability to fund them. We are like a household that spends its income regardless of how large it becomes and yet still wants more. Secondly, whilst all human endeavour must encompass failure, large state-run enterprises are bound to be more than normally susceptible to widely varying levels of standards and achievements and a fairly high level of inefficiency. The pessimist will have much support from those involved in private medicine — they have a lot to lose and will not give up their privileged position lightly. All this will lead him to the conclusion that the five dreary old reasons for long waiting-lists are quite correct and that such waiting-lists will be a permanent feature of British society which he could never change.

The optimist is angry when he sees suffering which he knows must be relieved. He searches hurriedly for a solution, alighting on the one closest to his prejudice and confidently asserts that if a particular action is undertaken all will be better. Solutions proposed include privatizing health care and introducing private insurance, totally separating private and NHS hospitals, closing down private hospitals, computerizing waiting-lists, appointing industrial style general managers to stamp out inefficiency, sacking lazy surgeons, etc. The optimist genuinely believes that his selected course of action would quickly eradicate or substantially reduce waiting time.

The realist is also angry when he sees thousands of his countrymen and women waiting in pain for straightforward and unequivocally helpful operations. He is sceptical about single and simple solutions. The realist appreciates that waiting-lists may never be completely eliminated, but he is not prepared to see the situation unnecessarily exaggerated. He sees that some of the long waiting and unnecessary suffering is caused by managerial and clinical inflexibility, incompetence, and even dishonesty. He seeks the support of the majority of ordinary clinicians, managers, and consumer representatives, to set in motion a string of activities which will significantly reduce large waiting-lists and long waiting time. His time-scale is two or three years and he knows that he has a painful fight on his hands. The realist will need a lot of support.

And where will my seven proposals leave Mrs G?

Virtually crippled because they were not implemented five years ago.

References

1. College of Health (1985). *Guide to hospital waiting lists 1985*. The College of Health and Inter-Authority Comparisons and Consultancy.
2. Searle, J. F. (1985). Putting the Health Service to rights. *The Times* 12 July.

Index

anatomy study 7, 25-6

balancing resources 33-5, 46-7
bed availability 31-2
bed use 40-2
BMA 14-15, 29
booked admission lists 22

causes of waiting-lists
  iceberg of demand 5, 20-7, 63
  inaccurate statistics 5, 8-18, 63
  industrial action 6, 49-51, 64-5
  inefficiency 6, 38-46, 64
  lack of resources 6, 27-35, 64
  private practice 6, 48-9, 51-61,
    64-5
College of Health 77-8
compensation for patients 83-4
complaining 69
computerizing waiting-lists 70-1
consultants contracts 85-7
contract surgery 71-3

day cases 75
district health authorities 3, 31, 39
Duthie Report 75-7

elderly 25-7
emergency admissions 42
ENT 12, 25-6, 41

general practitioners 13-14, 74
general surgery 11, 13, 25-6
good practice studies 84-5
gynaecology 9, 26, 41

health inspectorate 87

initiatives to reduce lists 68-79
international comparisons 30
investigating black spots 80

operating theatre
  availability 33
  scheduling 20-1
  use 42-5, 74
ophthalmology 6, 12, 25-6, 41
orthopaedics 3, 11, 15, 17, 24-6,
  75-7

politicians 24, 78-9
press and media 69-70
publishing information 81

specialty pleading 68
surgeons
  availability of 21, 33
  contracts 59-61
  workload 45-6

waiting-list fund 78-9
waiting-lists
  clerical review 10-12
  inflated lists 9-12
  size of lists 2-3
  studies 73-4
  underestimated 12-13
waiting time
  in-patients 16-18, 57-9, 87-8
  out-patients 13, 56-7, 82-3